I HAD MY UNDERWEAR ON THE ENTIRE TIME

*A Memoir of Discovering Family
through Genetic Genealogy*

MICHAEL & AMY BLAIR

Edition One
Advanced Readers Proof.
Not for sale

Chapters

Authors' Note

This is a work of non-fiction.
To protect the privacy of individuals, some names and
details in this story have been changed.

Introduction

In order to travel to Canada for vacation, I was unable to provide my original birth certificate and, as one of the requests made by the United States Government, I had to prove that I was circumcised. This is one of the many strange situations I have encountered by not having the original document of my birth. I am a nearly fifty year old man who has never seen his original birth certificate even though I have all the information of exactly who the first players in my life were, who made me, who raised me, who my parents are – still, I cannot hold in my hands the first document about the beginning of my existence.

The days of anonymity are over. Advances in genetic genealogy can provide anyone the ability to trace their family history in minutes for a mere $99.95 (plus shipping). Buyer be warned... services such as AncestryDNA or 23 and Me should really add a side-effect disclaimer to their advertising. *Warning: Results of your DNA test may cause the following side effects: anxiety, diarrhea, discovering unexpected siblings, dizziness, insomnia, heart palpitations, uncovering secrets Grandma took to her grave, nausea, thoughts of suicide, discovering your father had an affair, and/or all of the above.*

This book was written for adoptees and NPE's (Non-Parental-Event, or those who have found out that one of the parents who raised them was not biological), and for those who have discovered a genetic surprise. Those seeking can use the book as a guide to show different ways and techniques that the Internet and DNA testing sites can be of assistance in finding your birth family when county clerks refuse to unseal records or family members refuse to speak about the past.

For those who have discovered that their own beginning, middle, or end was not what they thought it was, you are not alone. Many people are discovering the same surprises and it leaves them hungry to find answers to their questions. This was written for those who have been misled into believing their life was something that it really wasn't and how when secrets come to surface that those results have consequences. My story will take you down a road less traveled, showing how when I refused to yield to the word "No," that I instead pushed the envelope where the responses I received were both rewarding and gut-wrenching.

Also, we wrote this story for those who believe the Right to Know Laws in their state should be passed and that all birth certificates be unsealed and access granted to those who seek them. Adoptees are the largest group of people who are denied ownership to their sealed birth certificates. Now with advances in scientific technology, virtually any American has the ability to search and find their birth parents. Anonymity is gone. Birth certificates hold no power of the unspoken secret and yet adoptees across the country are still denied the right of ownership to their first piece of paper.

Finally, for those who are not adopted, if you enjoy a good mystery or you are intrigued by seekers of decades-old secrets, you are also invited to come along on my journey that began from a mistake and ended with a bonus.

Dedication

FOR THE SEEKERS
You are not lost.
You are not a secret.
You are not alone.
You are brave.
You are allowed.
You are worth the truth.

All of our journeys are unique and, yet all of our journeys meet up along the way and intertwine.
Seek, ask questions, and learn.
Walk inside your story and own it.

This is my story but it is also the story of many.
This book is for us, those who were led astray but were curious enough to find our own road.

ONE

Waiting is not one of my strongest skills.

Whether it's waiting on test results, waiting on the birth of one of my children, waiting in line for concert tickets, or waiting to find out if I landed a job, waiting is not something I am very good at. "You are patiently impatient," my wife, Amy, would tell me.

I couldn't disagree. Even I had noticed the change in my behavior in the waiting time. I tended to get crabby, agitated and, in general, I was not a fun guy to be around. Keeping a good attitude was difficult for me while I waited.

I have become very familiar with the first floor of the Lucas Building in Des Moines, Iowa. Particularly Room #124, Vital Records, where I have lost countless hours waiting. I have been going in and out of this room since 1999, in pursuit of my first known document, my birth certificate. For over fifteen years I've come here to fill out the same request form at least a dozen times. I have paid $10 for each application, writing in different names that I thought it could be filed under. Over the years I have received many copies of my so-called birth certificate. But, in truth, it wasn't my *real* birth certificate. It was a certified copy of somebody's story of my birth, someone's account of when and where I was born, about who my parents were, thrown together on a piece of paper and then stamped with an official seal.

My original birth certificate—if one existed—was sealed. I am one person, who has lived with the identity of three names, all leading to multiple lines of ancestors, some willing to accept me and some wishing I had never been born.

I grew up in Altoona, Iowa, in a modest three-bedroom, one-bathroom house. There were five of us: Mom, Dad, me, plus Gina and Rachel, my two younger sisters. The house was small, always full of people, pets, food, and noise. My parents married young and, in many ways, they grew up with my sisters and me. As a child I didn't grasp how young they had been. I just didn't pay attention to those sorts of things.

My focus was on where I was in the moment, but as early as eight years old, something began to nag at me. My memories always surrounded living in that small house. I could barely remember a time when my sisters weren't present. All of my memories of childhood were full of my grandparents and the numerous dogs and cats we owned. But if I closed my eyes and thought way, way, way back—there was a memory I could almost touch. It wasn't of this house that I knew so well. My sisters weren't alive yet. And there was no person called "Dad." It was just me and my mom.

"Mikey." I opened my eyes and saw my mom looking down at me. I was young, two or three. "It's time to get up." I stretched my arms out so she could pick me up out of bed. But it wasn't my bed, it was her bed and as I snuggled into the crook of her neck, I watched the hallway and living room pass by of my grandparents' house. This is where we lived, with them.

My mom put me down and started tugging me into a pair of snow pants. I laughed as she tickled my feet, bringing each leg up and pulling them through the holes of the pants. I hung onto her shoulders and she shook me all the way in. I remember her giggle, her dark hair, her hand clasping mine softly as we walked out the door.

There was no dad. I was sure of that. I never remembered my

father in any of my early memories.

At the age of ten, in fifth grade science, my teacher was explaining to us the magic of inheritance and how every person gets twenty-three chromosomes passed on from each parent to make a complete human being. We all brought in photos to make a family tree and to tie in how certain traits from our parents and grandparents traced down to us. I proudly arranged pictures of my family, tiering them above me, in homemade construction-paper branches, and as my teacher walked around, she asked questions to the class: "Do you have your mother's smile?" "Do you have your grandpa's nose?" "Do you have your dad's hair color?"

My eyes went from one photo to the other. I could see similarities with my mom but not my dad . . . I raised my hand. "I don't think I look like my dad," I announced.

"Do you have his shoulders?" She placed her hands on her own shoulders.

I shook my head.

"Is he tall, like you?" Back then, I was the tallest in my class.

"No, he's short."

"Does he have your nose?" Her finger rested on her own nose.

I looked at my dad's photo and shook my head.

My teacher walked over and glanced over my shoulder. "Hmmm . . ." her eyes volleyed back and forth between me and my dad. "He has blue eyes," she pointed out. "And you do, too."

Ah, that was it. I nodded and drew a line from his eyes to mine. But my teacher stayed over me for a few seconds, still looking. Then she smiled and patted my back. She moved on to our grandparents and asked what we could see in them that we could see in ourselves.

Not knowing it at the time, that day in fifth grade science was my first step on the road to unlocking my past. Or, was I actually unlocking my beginning?

As with all of us, I came into this world a unique individual, a complete little human formed from the DNA passed on to me from my mother and my father. They, too, were born from their parents, receiving half their DNA from each, and so on and so on. I am made of the blueprints from generations that can be traced way back, names that I may never know. I was there, nestled in their blood and veins, just waiting to be born.

I have always belonged to someone. I have always belonged to them.

NOVEMBER 21, 2016

Three days before Thanksgiving, we were at home and Amy announced that it was time to brine the turkey. She was nervous this particular year because she had bought a twenty-eight-pound bird, the largest one she had ever cooked. That was the cue for me to hole up in my downstairs office while Amy stressed over calculating how early she had to wake up the next day.

In reality, Amy loves the anticipation and busy work that Thanksgiving provides her. It is the one holiday where we host both sides of our families. Amy is the youngest of six, and along with her Irish Catholic family and mine, it is not uncommon to have forty people crammed into our modest-sized house.

On that Monday evening, I felt a sizzle in the air. Amy hadn't lost her mind quite yet; she was still in the preparation mode, and the first thing on her checkoff list was to brine the bird. She had completed this ritual for years. From downstairs, I tracked her progress by the sounds above me. I heard her struggling with the large stock pot, filling her ten-gallon bucket with herbs and spices, I heard her chopping onions and apples and I knew when she was easing the turkey into the liquid because the faucet turned on. I listened as she filled the bucket with water and then waited five extra minutes after the faucet shut off. I figured the turkey was now safely secured in its brine and I could return upstairs, without the fear that Amy would ask me for help with something.

I opened the basement door and saw Amy, sitting at the kitchen table, her laptop in front of her, the glow from the screen illuminating her face. She looked up and grinned. "Oh my God, Michael. I found a way."

TWO

When I was twelve years old, my parents took me and my sisters graveyard tripping. We visited the graves of relatives whom I did not know. Great-grandparents, an aunt who had died as a toddler, and my paternal grandfather ... all people I had never met. At each stop, my personal goal was to chase my sisters around the headstones and scare them. When I got bored with that, I decided to play Cowboy and selected tall gravestones to jump on so I could ride them.

While playing, I managed to position myself behind my parents. They were gathered together, looking at the gravesite of my father's father, my Grandfather Blair. All I knew of him was he died when I was a baby. My parents were gazing at his marker, unaware that I was behind them.

"Forty-nine-years-old," my dad said, sadly. My mom stood quietly, staring at the marker and my eyes traveled to it, reading my Grandpa's name: Thomas John Blair.

"He was so young," my dad sighed. Then, after a pause, he continued, "I wish you and Mikey could have met him. You guys missed him by a year." He sniffled. "You and I met in, what? '74?"

"Yeah," my mom agreed.

I continued reading. Grandpa Blair died in April 1973. My parents were saying they met a year later in 1974. But ... how was that possible if I was born in 1972?

I heard my sisters giggling behind me, begging me to play hide-and-seek with them. So, I abandoned my parents and questions and, instead, returned to our game, pushing the information into the back of my mind. It was on the tip of my tongue to ask about it on the car ride home, but how does a twelve-year-old start that conversation? "Is Dad my real dad?" It sounded strange even thinking it. I mean, of course he had to be, right? It wasn't like there was somebody else hanging around, claiming that I belonged to him. So I didn't ask them. Maybe, at twelve, I wasn't ready for the answer. Or maybe it was because deep down, I already knew.

NOVEMBER 21, 2016

On that Monday evening, Amy sat down at her laptop. "Oh, my God, Michael. I found a way."

Immediately, I knew what she was talking about. With her words, I rolled my eyes and laughed out loud, all the while my shoulders stiffened and my stomach clenched.

We had been through false hopes in the past. Twenty-five years' worth of leads or clues or someone who we thought could help us perform a miracle with the minimal information we had accumulated. All of these hopes and dreams resulting in the same thing: a big, fat nothing.

But, as I rounded our kitchen island and reached up to make myself a drink, there was something different in Amy this time. She didn't say "I *think* I found a way," which was her classic "Amy-line." This time she said it with confidence, "I found a way."

Amy jumped up with excitement and acted out what she had just been doing. This was normal for my wife. By nature, she was an excitable person.

"I was standing here, brining the turkey and I turned on the faucet to fill up the bucket with water . . . ." she pulled the hose, disconnecting it from the faucet and pointed it down. "Then as I'm standing here, I look into the living room and the TV is on— " she pointed and I followed her finger. The TV was still on. "I see a commercial come on. It was for AncestryDNA. Have you heard of that?"

I shook my head.

"Okay, well there was this woman on and she's talking about how she completed a home DNA kit where she spits in a tube and sends it to Ancestry.com. When she gets her results she finds out she's not Nigerian after all, she's Scottish. And then she says that she has a cousin who lives two blocks away from her who she never even knew existed!" Amy flapped her arms and grinned big.

I stared at her, confused. "What?"

Amy sat down. "The woman found a *cousin* she didn't know existed. So, I googled 'Can AncestryDNA find family relatives?' and the answer is YES." She pointed to the computer screen. I hovered over her shoulder as she read about adoptees who were using Ancestry as a tool to find their bio-families. There were also a handful of happy reunion stories to accompany their journeys.

Amy was still smiling. "I found a way."

I nodded behind her. "Fuck yeah, you did."

Three days later, thirty-nine family members filled our home for Thanksgiving. My family gathered in the dining room, Amy's family spread throughout the kitchen and living room. Even though they were gathered together under the same roof, they divided into the familiar faces of their own people.

After the prayer, everyone grabbed a plate and mingled as they walked around the kitchen island.

"Ooh," Amy's sister Michelle cooed, "Who made this salad?"

My sister Rachel quietly replied, "I did."

"It looks so good," Michelle commented and everyone agreed.

Then they all retreated to their own families and old stories.

Amy and I exchanged silent looks that Thanksgiving. We both felt a change in the air. Maybe this would be our last Thanksgiving like this; that next year things could be very different. Good different or bad different? We didn't know.

Growing up, my family celebrated our holidays separately. One for the Blairs, one for my mother's family, the Langs. My parents did not mix their families together.

The Langs consisted of my grandparents, my Aunt Susan and her family. When we were together, there were eleven of us. Very manageable. I, being the oldest, divided most of my time between picking on my sisters and my two younger cousins while eavesdropping on the adult conversations. I had no one my age to hang out with.

My dad's side was quite different. He was one of five and when we gathered at my grandma's, it was a full house. Grandma had divorced Grandpa Blair in the 1960's and had remarried a fun-loving man, our Grandpa Peterson. I never knew my grandmother as anything except Grandma Peterson. So, for me, the Blair name always felt a bit foreign. There wasn't anything or anyone attached to it. We were not tethered to any other Blair in any generation before ours. It was like my dad and his siblings were plucked out of air and plopped down on earth, as the very first Blairs.

Unlike the Langs, the Blairs did have kids who were my age. I was still the oldest, but not by much. I had first cousins just a year or two younger than me and there were girls and boys to play with. A holiday without having to behead a Barbie doll and chase my sister with it was a good holiday for me.

Christmas of 1985, when I was thirteen, I was playing with my cousins in the basement when someone yelled down, asking if we wanted iced tea. The Blairs were crazy about iced tea, specifically instant Nestea Sweet Tea. They drank it by the gallon. My Uncle John, alone, could easily drink an entire jar all by himself in one sitting.

My cousins yelled, "Yeah, I want some tea!" My sisters yelled, "Me, too!" I yelled, "Yeah!"

My cousin Eric, who was my age, asked, "You like iced tea?"

I nodded. "Yeah."

"Huh," Eric shrugged. "I thought that was just a Blair thing."

"It is a Blair thing," I said.

"Yeah, but you're not a Blair."

"Yes, I am."

"Not a *real* one." Then, like he was speaking in slow motion, Eric said, "You're adopted."

My first instinct was to shout, "I am not!" But I didn't. I didn't say anything. I just stood there, staring at Eric. My mind skipped and suddenly I was back at the cemetery, standing behind my parents, hearing their whispered voices. Then I was sitting in fifth grade science with my teacher smiling down, patting my back. And finally I was two years old, and I was with my mom. No dad. Because back then, there was no one called Dad.

Eric waited a minute and when I didn't respond, he ran upstairs, leaving me alone in the basement with his words. I glanced up and caught my reflection in the mirror. Blond hair, blue eyes, tall, chunky. I looked like my sister Rachel and Rachel looked like my dad's side of the family. I wasn't adopted.

I squeezed my eyes tight and breathed deeply to slow down my racing emotions. I opened my eyes and looked again. From my hair to my eyes, to my rounded nose, to my thin lips, to my broad shoulders down to my size 10½ feet. I was almost six feet tall, two hundred pounds. My dad was maybe 5 foot 7. He was a thin, small-framed man. I didn't have his nose, his chin, his eyes. They might be blue, but they weren't his. I didn't have anything that was my dad's. All I had was his name.

I listened to my family above me, laughing and horsing around. And it slowly sank in—my dad wasn't my *real* dad. These people were not my *real* family. Eric wasn't teasing me. He was telling me the truth. I was adopted. And every single one of them knew it. All of them, except for me.

THREE

Amy and I have three daughters. At Christmastime 2016, Rosie was eighteen, Catey thirteen, and Jillian had just turned twelve. It had not been lost on me that what I was about to do would affect them as well. I actually took comfort in that knowledge. I was not alone. I had the three of them with me. Four, including Amy.

Over the years, as each girl turned ten years old, I took it upon myself to sit them down and have "the talk" with them.

"Your Papa Craig is not my biological father," I would tell them. "He's still your papa and always will be but we are not biologically connected to him."

Each girl's reaction was true to their personalities. Rosie was the first I told. Her eyes widened, she gasped. "What?" Pure shock. She paused, her young brain thinking. "Then who is your biological father?"

I shrugged. "I don't know."

Rosie blinked. "It's a mystery."

"Yes," I nodded. "We descend from mystery."

Catey's reaction was much more intellectual. "So, Papa Craig isn't your real dad?"

"He's not my biological father." I tried to avoid the phrase *real dad*. My dad was my dad. No one else.

"Then, who is your biological dad?"

"I don't know."

Catey hesitated. "How can you not know? How does Grandma not know?"

That was a hard question to answer a ten-year-old or even an adult. "I don't know," I answered honestly. "It's complicated."

My youngest daughter, Jillian, reacted exactly as I thought she would.

"Jill, your Papa Craig is not my biological father. He's still your papa and always will be, but another man is my biological father and I don't know who he is. I don't know his name or anything about him."

Jillian shrugged. "Okay." Then she asked to be excused so she could continue playing house with her sisters.

Christmas 2016, it was Jillian's turn to play Santa. "This one is for Dad." She handed me a small gift. I unwrapped it and turned the box around so they could see what Santa had brought me.

"What is that?" Rosie asked.

"It's an AncestryDNA kit." I replied. The box was smaller and lighter than I expected. It was white with small green boxes matched up together to create a DNA helix. There was a green leaf next to the Ancestry name and under that was the tagline "Where your story grows."

The girls looked confused.

"It's an at-home DNA kit. I'm going to spit in a tube and send it in. It will tell me what my Ethnicity is."

"Cool," they said.

"And it might be able to tell me who my biological father is."

The girls were quiet.

"Seriously?" Rosie asked.

I nodded.

She smiled. They all looked at each other and broke out into grins. "Cool," they said.

Then I put the box on our dresser and let it sit there for a couple of days. It was one thing to buy the kit and talk about completing it. It was another thing to actually do it. Opening it could be like literally opening a Pandora's Box. Once the spit was in there and I mailed it in, there would most likely be some kind of repercussions that would follow. I was someone who knew that a part of me was missing pieces to my puzzle. By spitting in a tube, I could be doing just the opposite to someone else: turning their world upside down, discovering that their life wasn't what they thought it was. I could be taking their fully, completed puzzle and shattering it.

The kit could hold the key to all my questions, but at what cost?

Two days after Christmas, Amy dug through our safe and retrieved what we referred to as "the black folder." Inside this folder was all of the information we had gathered on my biological father throughout the past twenty-five years. She opened it and pulled out a copy of my birth certificate and started reading it, questioning things, like we had done so many times before. "You're never going to find him," she said. Then she handed me the box. "Open it."

*
* *

When I was fourteen, my parents told me I had to go out and get a job. I had actually been previously employed when I was twelve, as a paperboy. When I was thirteen, my best friend Shawne and I had a weekly cartoon in the *Altoona Herald*, I was the illustrator and Shawne was the writer. However, now that I was fourteen, I was going to get my first real job, one where they made me fill out W-2s and took taxes out of my paycheck.

I applied and was hired at Adventureland, a theme park in my hometown. It was perfect as I could ride my bicycle to and from work. I was going to be on the sanitation team where I would have to keep the trash cans empty, sweep cement roads, and respond to "4A" calls. Those calls were the worst. The bodily fluid cleanup calls. Both ends.

"You'll need to bring in two forms of identification," my new boss explained. "Your social security card, your birth certificate, or a permit will work fine."

I went home and told my mom. I had yet to try for my driver's permit, so she dug out my recently issued Social Security card and my birth certificate. The next day, I took both to my new boss. She helped me fill out paperwork and made copies of my documents. When she got to my birth certificate, she stopped and stared at it for a few minutes.

"Are you adopted?" She didn't even hesitate, just asked it straight out.

I shook my head. "No."

"Oh. Well, your birth certificate is strange."

I had never seen a birth certificate in my life so I had no idea what a normal one looked like versus the one that I had. "What's strange about it?"

"First, it says it's a Delayed Certificate of Birth so it's not your original birth certificate." She pointed to the top of the paper. "Second, it has your mom listed as your mother in 1972 but you see these three lines?" I followed her finger toward the bottom. "This is where your father's name is supposed to be. There are three entries here—two of them are blank, the one for 1972 and 1977 and then your father's name is on the third line but it says it was entered on January 30th, 1979. That's seven years after you were born." She looked at me. I'm not sure what my face said but she shrugged it off. "It's probably nothing. I have just never seen a birth certificate like this. Maybe you want to ask your mom about it."

I folded the paperwork under my jacket and rode my bike home. When my mom walked in the door, I dangled my birth certificate in front of her face and told her that my new boss had questioned if my birth certificate was real. "Why does it say Delayed Certificate of Birth on it?" I asked.

My mom was quick. "I lost your birth certificate a long time ago when we moved. This is what they look like when they replace an original birth certificate. It's absolutely real." She snatched it out of my hands, stuffed it into her filing folder, and took the folder into her bedroom.

After that, when my parents left the house and I was alone, I would wander around until I found myself sitting in front of their closet. I would carefully pull out the file folder and snoop through it. I don't know what I was looking for, I suppose something that said "adoption" or "Michael something-else for a last name." I never found anything of importance.

Just several copies of my Delayed Certificate of Birth.

* *
* *

"Spit," Amy said.

I had the box unwrapped and was holding a little plastic vial. I popped the end off and positioned the funnel under my mouth and worked my saliva glands. A lot of spit came out on the first attempt, but it only reached the halfway mark. I was surprised at how much saliva the little tube needed. After I reached the fill line, I replaced the top with a cap filled with green preservation liquid. I read the instructions carefully as I tightened the cap and then shook my saliva, mixing it with the liquid. I labeled the tube and placed it into the mailing envelope. Then I walked out to our mailbox and for one second, I hesitated. I thought maybe I needed to give up some good vibes so I kissed the box and said out loud, "Good luck, spit! Hope you find my dad!" And I put the flag up. Our mail lady arrived about an hour later and Amy and I watched from our front window as she took my sample and drove away with it.

"Now we wait," I sighed. Oh, how I hated to wait. But this time, I waited with hope. I hoped this time my efforts wouldn't lead me back to a stack of papers but rather to an actual living, flesh, breathing, blood relative.

FOUR

I have great memories of my younger childhood. Warm, fuzzy memories, like you're supposed to have. I remember birthdays where my mom would make a cake from a mold—one year a happy clown, another a bright red ladybug—and it would be decorated perfectly. I remember family outings to the drive-ins, rowdy barbeques, walks on long summer nights, and Saturday morning cartoons curled up in our pajamas.

My memories of adolescence are a chaotic blur. Truth be told, when I still my body and close my eyes, my mind takes me back to high school and friends. Driving in cars, eating junk food, laughing at lame jokes, playing silly pranks on each other. My mind is flooded with the smells of cafeteria food, roads traveled on too fast, part-time jobs, vinyl records, and the laughter of my best buddies.

Being with my friends was the best part of my adolescence years. It was them, a collective gang of misfits, who got me through it.

When I switch the gears in my memory to my family, it is a forceful maneuver and not an enjoyable one.

As an adult who has been married for more than twenty-seven years, I now grasp the complexities of the high highs and the low lows of the rollercoaster called marriage. I would never pretend to understand my parents' union as I wasn't part of it. I know now that there are moments in a marriage where the rollercoaster is going up, up, up with anticipation, your hands are above your head, and you're squealing in delight and then the next day you can be clinging to the sides of the car as it skids around a dangerous curve. Sometimes all we can do is hang on.

As a teenager, I didn't have the experience of a lifetime living with one person to understand what my parents were going through. I was preoccupied with myself most of the time, but from my perspective, they argued a lot. There were fights that would get so bad that I would lay in bed at night, afraid to get up to use the bathroom. There were threats of divorce and for a short period of time, my dad moved out and got an apartment. My sisters and I were pleased about it. We visited him there. He seemed proud of his new space as he gave us the grand tour. Personally, I was thrilled. I *wanted* them to get a divorce. The fighting had stopped, there were no more tears, and my mother seemed happy and strangely free.

A few months went by and then, one day, I came home from school and my dad was sitting on the living room couch. He was slurping a soup bowl and drinking a beer. Nothing was ever mentioned to us about how or why he was back. My mother didn't sit us down and ask how we felt about Dad returning home. One day he just showed up on the sofa and never left. With that, the fighting found its way back in the corners of the house and the yelling and the tears returned along with his luggage.

Throughout this time, there was a growing strain between me and my parents. I knew by this point that my dad wasn't my biological father, but I wasn't asking and they weren't telling. On the outside, I appeared withdrawn and uninterested, but on the inside, I was burning with anger. The only way I could direct my rage was to direct it toward my parents. Specifically, my dad.

Whatever he liked, I hated. If he liked war movies, I liked comedies. If he liked basketball, I thought it was the dumbest game ever played. If he talked to me about joining the Army, I told him I was moving to Canada. If he talked about God, I told him no such thing existed. I wanted to make myself as opposite of him as I possibly could and I wanted him to feel that disconnect, too.

One night, my dad and I were in the living room. He was engrossed in a football game while I was reading a comic book. We both stood to get a snack and as we rose, he looked me up and down and said, "It's too bad you never took to football, Mike. You could have been one hell of a linebacker. You sure are built for it. Look at those shoulders. You could have taken a hit. It's a damn shame you never wanted to play."

I towered over him and looked down. "Did you play football, Dad?"

"No."

I frowned. "Why not?"

"Because I wasn't built for it."

"But I am?"

We had a minute-long staring contest. I waited for him. He eyed me long and hard and I felt it in my gut—he knew that I knew. But he wouldn't say a damn word.

It was never the spoken word that did the most damage in our house, it was the unspoken.

When your parents surround you with untrue stories of where you come from and build your life around believing one group of people are your ancestors—their blood, their history, their name—belongs to you—but you know that it's nothing but a bunch of secrets and lies, bullshit fabrications made up to trick you into thinking you are someone you're not . . . well, those decisions shake the very foundation of who you think you are.

When it's your family who knew the entire time, you start to realize how hard they all must have worked to keep the secret buried. My mother, my father, my grandparents, aunts, uncles, and cousins . . . it begs the question: What really was the nature and quality of our relationships? They deemed me not worthy enough to know my own origin story and so my family chose to keep it from me.

Then, one day it happened.

It was the summer after I graduated high school. My dad signed me up to receive information on the Army and Marines, so recruiters were calling the house daily. I got a job at McDonald's making pancakes but hated getting up at 5am, so I quit after three weeks.

Frustrated, my dad would drive me downtown on his way to work and drop me off on a random street. "You go walk into every single building and start applying. I will pick you up right here at five o'clock."

I would spend the afternoon wandering downtown Des Moines, sitting under the Claes Oldenburg Umbrella sculpture, reading for a couple of hours. I would run the skywalks and look at the art displays, I grabbed lunch from a hot dog stand, and I would go inside and sit in lobbies of large insurance companies until 5pm.

My dad couldn't figure out why a dumb kid like me wasn't getting any job offers.

I was two weeks into not doing a damn thing with myself. I was in my favorite position and place, lying on the sofa, watching TV in the living room. My mom was vacuuming the carpet around my lazy feet. Without any warning, she quietly shut the vacuum off and took a breath. "Craig is not your real dad."

I looked at her. "Yeah, I know."

"You do?"

"Yeah."

"Oh." She paused. "Okay." Then she started the vacuum up and continued with her cleaning.

I can't explain why I didn't say anything else at that time. Maybe it was the moment. Maybe it was because it was such an important thing to tell someone and she did it like it was an afterthought, like she was telling me she was going to make lasagna for dinner. Maybe it was because I was beyond angry at both of them and I wanted her to know that it didn't matter if she told me or not. I already knew. I didn't offer her any information on how I had come to my conclusion. I would keep that from her, as my own secret. Make her wonder how I had figured it out.

My sister Gina came home later that day. My parents had gone off to their second and third jobs. I was still lying on the sofa, still watching TV. I looked up at Gina and said, "Guess what Mom told me today? She said Dad isn't my biological dad."

Gina blinked.

I went on. "You know, like dad is not my *real* dad."

Gina nodded. "I know."

"You know? How do you know?"

Her small shoulders shrugged. "Mom told me. She told me and Rachel."

"You guys knew?" I sat up. I was furious. Not only did my *entire* family know, but my *younger* sisters, too? Lies hidden from me in plain sight. Everyone knew. Except me. The one person who mattered.

For one week we lived under the same roof, knowing we all finally knew. I imagined what it was like when my mom told my dad. I envisioned her waiting for him to come home and her loudly whispering, "He already knew!" I wondered what my dad's face looked like. I wished I could have seen it—the amazement and realization that I was smarter than he thought I was. I had already figured it out. Neither one of them had fooled me.

That's what I wished I could feel like. Strong and empowered. But instead, I felt broken and betrayed and like I didn't belong there anymore, if I ever had.

A few days later a fight broke out. I was done. I got in the middle of it, words were said, I was told I wasn't welcome anymore. I left the house on foot. I had nowhere to go, no job, no car, no money, no clothes. I was walking into the unknown, which was fine by me because I was so used to the unknown now that I embraced it as my identity.

I was the unknown.

FIVE

I went on through most of my days without much thought to my ancestry test. On the weekends, when things quieted down, restlessness would set in.

"Four to six weeks," Amy reminded me.

In the middle of the night, I found myself Googling things like "On average how long does it take to get your Ancestry DNA results?" Answer: four to six weeks. I kept hoping it would be like those rare times when you walked into a busy restaurant and the hostess says, "It will be about an hour." So you sit down to wait and five minutes later your table is ready.

In the beginning, I would get a progress report from Ancestry every other day. *Your Ancestry kit has been activated! Your sample has arrived! Your sample is in the lab! Your sample is being processed . . .*

And then, nothing.

* *
*

In the weeks that followed after my mom's admission that my dad wasn't my biological father and then, of course, being kicked out of the house, I spent my time homeless and then jumping from friend to friend's house until one of them took me in for a few days. All of my friends still lived with their parents so my friend Tavis convinced his mom to let me stay with them for a week until I figured things out. On the third day of living with them, I made a list of goals:

1. Find a place to live.

2. Get a job.

3. Buy a car.

I thought about it a minute and then added one more:

4. Get a girlfriend.

Two days later I called my Grandma Lang. She simply asked, "Where are you?" I gave her the address and within the hour, she picked me up. I went home with her in the same clothes and shoes that I had been wearing when I left my parents' house.

Grandma and Grandpa Lang had been a constant in my life. They were quite literally my rock. They were whom I lived with from the time I was born until I was four years old. I had a uniquely close relationship with them. Growing up, it was them that I was concerned about disappointing, not my parents. It was them that I wanted to impress, to hear their praise. And it was them that I listened to when I needed schooling.

My Grandma Lang didn't ask or talk about the fight that I had with my parents, although it was obvious that she knew everything. Instead, she took me home, made me dinner, and told me, "Tomorrow I will bring you to work with me and we will get you a job there."

She worked at America's Pharmacy, a mail order pharmacy, where the job I applied for required me to stand in an assembly line, in front of a conveyor belt, where prescriptions would filter down. Someone needed to grab the labeled bottle, count the medication out, and fill the bottle before it proceeded down the belt to a pharmacist.

I applied with no experience and was hired on the spot.

For the next few months, I refused to speak to my parents.

Thanksgiving and Christmas came and went and while I lazily mingled with my family, I spoke tersely to my parents, only answering yes and no to questions when asked. I had my nineteenth birthday and refused to spend any time with them. I continued on, living with my grandparents, working at the pharmacy, and pretending to be happy. I bought an old, beat-up station wagon at an estate sale for three hundred dollars. The owner's daughter handed me the keys and title. I signed it, proud that I owned something that no one could take away from me. It was big enough that if things got bad again, I could live in it. Not comfortably, but it was a real option.

I got in and started him up. The smell from the inside almost doubled me over. I wondered if the dead guy who owned him before me had actually died in the car. Affectionately, I named him Old Man.

In that moment, my relationship with Old Man was the happiest one I had.

Seven months after I started working with Grandma, I walked in on a Monday morning in May and found that a group of four girls who I had become friends with had increased to five. Amy will tell the story that she was home from college and she and her two best friends wanted to work together so she joined the mail order pharmacy for the summer just to have fun with her friends.

She didn't count on me being there.

The minute I saw her, I knew she was going to fulfill my #4 goal of getting a girlfriend. My list would be complete! I quietly asked around about her and one of her friends told me, "That's Amy. She's bubbly."

When Amy tells her side of the story, she says that she gave no seriousness to my advances and thought of me as annoying until one day I walked to the vending machine, slid my money in, and selected a Twix bar. When the candy dropped down to the bottom, I bent down to grab it and my jeans pulled down beyond my waistline.

For a quick second, my butt crack was exposed.

Amy swears in that moment, she knew. She leaned over to her best friend Chris and said, "You see that guy? I'm going to marry him one day."

Nothing says "this one is good marriage material" like a sweet-looking butt crack.

It wasn't long into our relationship that I confided in her the story of how I ended up living with my grandparents and why I didn't want her to meet my mom and dad.

Amy's advice was straightforward, "You need to ask your mom about your biological father."

"I don't think she knows who he is."

Amy shrugged. "Maybe she doesn't. But she has to remember how she met him and how you were conceived. I'm sure she knows at least his first name. She has details. Figuring out who he is may not be as impossible as you think. But, first, you need to ask her."

I disagreed with Amy's confidence that finding my biological father wouldn't be impossible. But I agreed with her that if I wanted answers for my own peace of mind, I would need to talk to my mother. It took me over a year to get up enough nerve to talk to her. By this time, Amy had decided to leave the college she was studying at and moved home to go to school and be closer to me. I was feeling pressure from my grandparents that I had lived with them long enough. Once again my welcome had been worn out. I asked Amy if she would move in with me and she replied, "No. I mean, if we were engaged, I suppose I would. But I'm not just going to live with my boyfriend."

So, I bought her a ring and we moved in together. It was during this time that I decided it was time to ask my mother about my biological father. I was getting married and the tension between me and my parents was still palpable. Until I brought it up and tried to get answers, the strain would remain. I drove over to my parents' house and found my mom alone. It took thirty minutes of small talk before I brought it up. "I wanted to ask you a couple of questions about my biological father," I began. "What do you know about him?" I held my breath. My stomach turned. I was nauseous.

"I don't know anything about him." My mom paused. "I don't know who he is."

I blinked and tried to keep a clear head. I needed to think of open-ended questions to keep her talking. I didn't want that one question to be the end of our conversation and have this swept back under the rug. "Okay, well, can you tell me how you met him?"

My mom quieted and then she began her story.

Over the years, I will go back to this story again and again, picking it apart, looking for clues, reading things that maybe I missed. I will visualize it in my head as I recall it later for Amy and my friends. I will think of it as I drift off to sleep. This story will slice through my brain as I hear the words, "You're going to be a daddy." I will quickly recite the story as I talk to private investigators, as I fill out paperwork for Iowa's vital records department, as I consult with attorneys and as I talk to other adoptees. I will ramble off this story to therapists. I will take all of the unknown parts of me and try to squeeze in these words, as if they might complete me in some pathetic way. The questions of how I got to be here and the mystery that I was born from will fall back to these words from my mother. And for the next twenty-five years, it is this story that will haunt me every single day.

SIX

It was evening when I arrived at my parent's house, but it had turned to night when my mother and I began talking. She was not completely willing to talk right away. She seemed tired and like this was what she had been dreading—to tell me her side of things, her version of the truth.

I sat down as she paced in front of me. "I was seventeen and a junior in high school." I nodded. I knew she was a teenage mom. Even before I figured out that my dad was not my biological father, I understood my mother had been young. Very young. I had seen pictures taken of her, in a *Before Michael* state of time, where she seemed happy and carefree. Then there were pictures of her two years later, where she was more experienced and mature, a darkness in her eyes, tired-worry lines already setting in, a new era of time, *After Michael*. But to hear her say she was seventeen, a junior in high school really set the tone. She was a young teenager, naïve to the world around her.

"I was walking down Grand Avenue ... close to Grandma and Grandpa's old house —"

I nodded. I knew the house.

"Our typewriter was broken and was at a repair shop, so I was checking to see if it was done. This guy pulled up beside me and

31

offered me a ride. He was on a motorcycle. I jumped on the back and he took me over to the store and he waited for me. The typewriter wasn't ready. So I came outside and we drove around for a while."

"How were you going to carry a typewriter and ride on the back of a motorcycle?" I asked, my brain already logically breaking down the story.

My mother shrugged. "I don't know. I didn't think that far ahead."

I nodded.

"He ended up taking me back to where he lived. He shared a house with four or five other guys. They all worked together. They were having a party there and I hung out with him. We had sex—it was my first time ever doing it—and afterward, he took me home."

"That was the only time you saw him?"

"No. He took my phone number and he would call me. I didn't have his number, he only had mine. He called me about a month later and we hung out." She paused. "We had sex that time, too."

"He took you back to his house?"

"No, that time was in my bedroom. At Grandma and Grandpa's house."

I blinked. "Really? Wow."

"Yeah, and then I didn't hear from him for a while. By the time he called again, I was pregnant. I told him over the phone that I was pregnant and my parents were really mad." She stopped, took a breath. "He said not to worry, that he would come over and we would work it out. We hung up but he never came over and I never heard from him again."

Seventeen, I reminded myself. This was a major turning point for her, everything she knew was going to change. She wouldn't graduate from school because the administration wouldn't allow her to attend. She wouldn't go to college because she had to get a job to support me. In a few years, she would meet my dad and get pregnant with my sister and end up marrying him because he stayed. Her life would be very difficult and she would have to sacrifice her future because I was growing inside her.

"What—what was his name?" I asked.

"I don't remember."

I frowned. "He called you up and would ask you out."

"I never had his phone number, he only had mine."

I nodded. "Yeah, but when he called, wouldn't he give you a name? I mean, how did you know it was him?"

"It was an easy name. Like, maybe, John."

"His name was John?"

She shook her head. "Maybe. I don't know."

I didn't want her to stop talking. "What did he look like?"

"Like you. He was tall with light brown hair. He had muscles." She thought for a minute. "He smoked."

I sat, processing. My mind kept coming back around to the name thing. "John? No last name?"

She shook her head. "I think it began with an S. Smith?"

"John Smith?" I snapped. "Seriously? John Smith?"

My mother didn't reply. She walked out of the living room and into the kitchen, leaving me alone for a few minutes. I wasn't even sure when she returned. I looked over and there she stood, waiting on me. She was only five-feet-tall, her dark hair brushed away from her face. She had bright red lipstick on.

"How old was he?"

"I would guess," she began, "he was a couple of years older than me. He lived on his own. He seemed around nineteen or twenty. I don't remember asking his age."

"Did he know that you were in high school?" I asked.

"I don't know. I don't remember talking about that." She thought for a minute. "He did come over to my house and he saw that I lived with my parents. They were home."

"Grandma and Grandpa met him?" I tried to keep the surprise out of my voice.

"I wouldn't say met him but they were home when he came to pick me up." We were quiet for a while. Absorbing. "It wasn't you; it was me," she said. "He didn't want me. I told him I was pregnant, and I never heard from him again, but it was me that he was running from. I don't . . ." she trailed off. "When I met your dad he said he would adopt you. He's the one who wanted you. He wanted us."

"I know," I said. "He stepped up. And I appreciate that."

My mom didn't seem to hear me. "We had to put an ad in the paper and see if he would come back to claim you."

"Who? John Smith?"

"Yeah," she replied.

"You guys put an ad in the paper? What paper?"

"I don't remember. The judge made us do it. So your dad could adopt you."

"When did you do that? What year?"

She shrugged. "Mid-seventies."

"If you didn't know his name, who was the ad addressed to?"

"I don't know."

I nodded, adding everything up in my head. "So, a tall guy with light brown hair, nineteen or twenty, muscles, rode a motorcycle, a smoker, named John Smith?"

She nodded. "It wasn't Smith. But I think it started with an S."

"Where was his house?"

"On the east side."

"Of Des Moines?"

She nodded.

"*Where* on the east side?"

"I don't remember."

"And you're sure his name was John?"

"No," she said. "I don't remember his exact name. It was an easy name. I mean, I'm sure at the time, I knew it. I just... don't remember anymore."

"You sure don't remember much, do you?"

My mother threw a hard look my way. "I've told you everything that I know!" Her chin wobbled and her eyes teared up.

"Okay," I said. "I believe you." But I didn't. Not a hundred percent.

She threw her arms up and they slapped on her side. "What more do you want? I told you everything I know! I told him I was pregnant... and he didn't stick around! He wasn't a good guy!"

"What does that mean? Did he... did he force himself on you?" I asked. *Please say no, please say no, please say no...*

"No," she replied. "He just... he lied to me. He said he was going to come over and he sounded like he was going to help me, and I believed him. Then he didn't show up." She was quiet a few seconds. "I don't regret having you or anything, but I don't regret how I handled things, either. I know you think we lied to you but that's just how people dealt with situations like that."

Situations like that? My life was not a situation. "I don't *think* you guys lied to me, Mom. You guys *did* lie to me."

She scoffed. "Well... we lied to you about Santa Claus, too!"

I blinked. "It's not the same thing."

"It's not much different. Parents lie to their kids all the time about all sorts of things."

My body responded faster than my brain. I balled my hands into fists and then took a moment and released them. I steadied my breathing. "You could have told me before, Mom." The tone of my voice had changed. Sharper. "You and Dad didn't have to lie to me my whole childhood about who..." I was going to say "my father was" but instead I diverted to, "about who I was."

"You're *you*. You've always been *you*. Nothing has changed. Where you come from doesn't matter when you're not part of it."

I glared at her. "How would you know? You grew up knowing who you came from. I grew up always knowing something wasn't right. I just didn't know that it was me that wasn't right!"

"I didn't tell you because I didn't want you to hate me," she said. She was crying now. "And now you hate me."

I took a couple of breaths to cool my jets. I took too long, though. My mom bolted down the hallway, into her bedroom, and slammed the door. I followed her, lingering outside of her bedroom. Through the door, I could hear her cries turn to sobs. This, I was not good at. I hated it when Amy cried, I never knew what to say. I certainly didn't know what to do with my mother bawling her eyes out. I tapped the door. "Mom." She didn't respond. I waited. "Mom, I don't hate you. I love you." I waited a few more minutes but she didn't come out. "I believe you," I said. "And I know..." What? What did I know? I knew she was seventeen. I knew she was just a kid. "I know you did your best."

My mother didn't open her door. She stayed locked in her bedroom, choosing to stay away from me. I gave her another thirty minutes and then finally left for the night. I drove home and told Amy about the conversation. She made notes in a notebook. "This will help us to remember. You'll forget what you asked and what she said over time," Amy explained.

I nodded. She was probably right. I was so overwhelmed, I felt like I was already losing words.

"Do you feel any better knowing what you know now?" Amy asked.

I shook my head. "Not really."

"Are you glad to have heard her side of the story?"

I nodded. "Yeah."

"We have more to work with than we did before." At her core, Amy was addicted to hope. She hung on tight to that hope throughout the next twenty-five years, like it was the only lifeline that could lead us to him.

"There is nothing my mom said that can help us."

"We have a name," Amy pointed out.

"John Smith?" I laughed.

Amy pulled out a black folder and stuck the notebook in it. "It sounds like your grandparents met him. They must have a memory of the encounter. You've never talked to them about how they felt or what they did when your mom told them she was pregnant."

Huh. She was right. "No, I've never asked them."

"Your parents also took an ad out. There should be some kind of record of it. I think the library has old newspapers on microfiche."

"Yeah." My voice raised an octave. Maybe there was something here that could help us.

"First, though, you're going to have to talk to your grandparents."

"Okay," I agreed. "That's a good idea."

Amy paused. "So, what was your overall feeling about the conversation?"

I thought a long moment. "I felt like my mom is protecting someone. And that someone isn't me."

SEVEN

January 2017 was the longest month ever. We celebrated New Years and waited. We partied on Amy's birthday at the end of the month. And waited. It had been five weeks since mailing my sample into Ancestry and three weeks since I had received a text. I began to wonder if my results had been lost or if they just forgot to send a text stating that my results were completed. I started checking the website daily. Sometimes two or three times a day.

Amy was more proactive. After I sent my sample in, the Ancestry website invited me to build a family tree, so Amy and I sat down and began my maternal side. It started out as a fun activity for the two of us, but soon we became obsessed. One branch on my Grandpa Lang's side went way back—further and further than I could have ever imagined. It became actual investigative work, but it kept Amy busy and she would update me on things she found. "You're twenty-fourth great grandfather was King Henry the II!" She yelled out one day. Indeed, it looked like he was. I was a descendant of Charlemagne. There was a line in my tree that could be traced back to 245 A.D. 245—as in a REAL YEAR. Gambara re dei Lombards, my 57th great-grandmother.

Today, when I'm visiting with friends and the topic of their ancestry comes up, they often tell me, "I can trace my mom's side back to the 1800s." I just smile and say, "Bitch, hold my beer."

I have heard people describe days that change their lives starting out as "any other day..." and that's exactly what happened on this Saturday. It started out as any other day. I woke up, Amy and I had errands to run, the girls had friends to see, money to spend. We ran around that afternoon and I grabbed a pizza for everyone that night. Bedtime came early. Around ten, I went upstairs, took my nighttime sleeping meds, and crawled into bed. Amy joined me a few minutes later. She turned on the TV and we snuggled in to enjoy Saturday Night Live's monologue. Kristen Stewart was the guest host.

Amy was starting to pass out. I felt my own eyes pulling down when I heard my phone buzz. I glanced at it.

10:55pm. A single-line text: *Your AncestryDNA Results Are In!*

"My results are in," I whispered.

Amy was turned toward me. Her eyes widened and she propped herself up. "Open it!"

"I am!" I clicked on the app icon. *Michael, the AncestryDNA results you've been waiting for are here*! It was just like they knew I had been waiting and checking and refreshing my screen three times a day! *You're about to discover your Ethnicity estimate, get a unique look at your family's journey, and maybe even connect with long-lost relatives! We're so excited for you!* I was glad somebody was! Personally, I thought I might throw up. I clicked on DNA Results.

There were two choices: Ethnicity and DNA Matches.

"Go to Ethnicity first," Amy suggested.

I clicked on it. "Scandinavian, England/Wales, and Ireland. I'm a boring white guy," I said, somewhat disappointed.

"You're only three percent Irish?" Amy noted. Her family came from Ireland. In a couple of years, Amy would purchase a DNA kit for her own father. One hundred percent Irish. One hundred percent. "My dad will be so disappointed. We'll just tell him you're Irish. We won't mention the percentage."

"Scandinavian?" I was surprised. "I'm a Viking."

"You've always liked stories about Vikings," Amy raised her eyebrows.

She was right. I did.

Amy placed her hand on my arm. "Okay, now go to DNA Matches."

I exited Ethnicity and went back to the main screen. I clicked on DNA Matches and we both watched as my iPhone changed images. There was a list of names in front of me. The top name was smooshed together, like one word. It was the name of a woman whom I had never heard of before: LouisaSchmidt, Close Family-1st cousin.

"Look!" Amy shouted. "You got a first cousin match! One of that lady's uncles must be your father!"

And this is the strangest part of it all—after all those weeks of waiting for my DNA results, after years of searching for my biological father, after a lifetime of not feeling like I knew who I was, Amy and I both said, "Okay, we have to go to sleep. We'll look at it in the morning."

Seven hours later we woke up at the same time and simultaneously threw the covers off our bodies and fought for who got to hit the shower first.

I won.

FEBRUARY 5, 2017

It was Super Bowl Sunday. The Patriots versus the Falcons (spoiler alert: Patriots won). Our next-door neighbors were hosting a Super Bowl party later in the evening. It was bacon themed. Amy had baked a maple bacon cheesecake the day before, so we had the next seven hours to devote to finding my biological father.

Amy cracked open her laptop and placed the notebook, which she had kept in the black folder for twenty-five years, next to her. "What's her name again?"

I clicked on the Ancestry app from my phone. I couldn't click fast enough. Amy hovered over my screen. There was a pink icon, no picture, with the name LouisaSchmidt, all together, not separated by any spaces. I clicked on Louisa's name and it took me to another screen, confirming our DNA results. Predicted relationship: Close Family-1st Cousin. From there we were able to see that Louisa had joined Ancestry in February 2006 and she had an extensive family tree built.

"She's probably the family genealogist," Amy stated, like she just knew.

We noticed that Louisa had not been active nor had signed into her Ancestry account since September 2016. That had been four months ago. The only other information we were able to see was that Louisa was from Grapevine, Washington. A long way from Iowa.

"Shit," I said. "There's like one, two, three . . . there's like twelve states between us."

In our six weeks of waiting, Amy had watched several YouTube videos from the Barefoot Genealogist, explaining *How to read your AncestryDNA results*. Amy had me click on a little, tiny "i" that was near Louisa's name. This took me to another screen, which listed two important things:

1. The amount of DNA segments and centimorgans that Louisa and I shared
2. How confident Ancestry was in their predictions.

The next few minutes Amy gave me a crash course on centimorgans. She showed me a chart of possible relatives and how many centimorgans you would need to share with an individual to determine how you might be related. The higher the centimorgans, the closer the relation.

"If this were your biological father, you would share about half of your centimorgans with him, which would be about thirty-five hundred," Amy pointed to a green chart. "So, if this lady is your first cousin, you would share between six hundred to twelve hundred."

I glanced at the shared centimorgans between Louisa and me. "One thousand, nine hundred, seventeen." I frowned.

Amy went back and forth between my results and the chart. "Oh, I see—Ancestry words that weird. They don't mean she's your close family *and* she's a first cousin. They mean she is at least a first cousin *to* a close family member. So she could be closer, like an aunt or a half-sister or something like that." Amy pointed to the chart. The amount of centimorgans did show that my relationship with Louisa would be that of an aunt/nephew, grandmother/grandson, or half-siblings. Amy wrote the three possibilities down in the notebook.

Then we looked at how confident Ancestry had us calculated at. *Extremely Confident (virtually 100%)*. So, no real margin of error. This woman and I were definitely related.

"Okay." Amy turned to her laptop and typed "Louisa Schmidt, Grapevine, Washington" into Google. The first line listed her address. The second line told us her age. According to Google, Louisa was sixty-seven. Amy quietly reached over and scratched out grandmother and half-sibling. She circled *aunt*. Twice.

The third line was an obituary. Amy clicked on it. "Oh, my God!" We both yelled. Amy's hand covered her mouth. I scooted my chair around the table and we both stared quietly at the computer screen.

The obituary was for a man named George Schneyder. His face, his eyes, his nose, his lips . . . "That's my grandfather," I whispered.

Amy scrolled down the obit. He lived to be eighty-nine years old and had died of lung cancer. He married in 1946 in Lawrence, Iowa. He spent time in the US Navy, he was a farmer, retired in 1980. He died in October 2008. He was survived by his wife and ten children, onçe which was Louisa.

Amy copied his wife's name: Pauline Schneyder and opened a new tab. She pasted the name into Google and pushed enter. Pauline's obituary popped up. She died in June of 2010. "Oh, no," Amy said regretfully.

I blinked. These people were my grandparents. I swallowed. "I missed them," I said. George by eight years; Pauline by six. "Twenty-five years of searching . . . and I missed them."

Amy read through Pauline's obituary. Lots of the same information as George, except she had been a teacher. "Maybe that's where I got my teaching gene," I joked, already trying to find similarities. Pauline was a thin woman. My daughter Rosie had her jawline. There was a list of survivors: Ten children. Five girls. Five boys.

Amy flipped her notebook and started a new sheet for each man. She labeled the top of the page with their name: Don, Bill, Edward, Wayne and Marty. She dragged the mouse across Louisa's name. Pauline's obituary stated Louisa lived in Skyland, Oregon, not Grapevine. Amy shrugged. "Maybe she moved. It has been six years."

Amy then set out to find out as much as she could about the five men. Her first priority was to find out how old was each one in 1971. It was both surprising and unsettling, everything we could find out just by simple Google searches. It also helped that their last name was pretty uncommon. The youngest of the five, Marty, was only ten in 1971 so Amy scratched through his name and concentrated on the other four.

Don was twenty-five, Bill twenty-four, Edward nineteen, Wayne eighteen, and my mother had been seventeen. Amy then brought up Facebook and plugged in each man's name. Don was a quick find. He wasn't on Facebook, but his wife was, and Don was her profile picture. Amy hit photos and we looked at a few from a wedding. "He looks like you," Amy said. She highlighted our jawlines, the scruff of his beard was just like mine. She then scrolled through and found Happy Anniversary wishes. "They were married in 1969."

We both winced. "Let's try another brother," Amy typed in Bill Schneyder. He had his own Facebook page. We brought up his photo. Amy and I tilted our heads to the left. "Eh . . ." Did Bill and I look like we were related? Sure. Did we look like father and son? No.

Amy couldn't find Wayne but found his son Nate. Nestled in Nate's photos was one lone picture of his dad. Wayne was very blond with sharp angles squaring out his face. He was more muscular than I was but had striking blue eyes. "He kind of looks like you. You guys definitely have the same eye color, but his son..." Amy clicked on Nate's picture. He and I looked a lot alike. "Big possibility," Amy said. "And he's only one year older than your mom."

We typed in the last brother, Edward. He and his wife had a shared Facebook account. "Somebody has trust issues," I chuckled. Amy clicked on photos and, again, we saw another wedding. Then they were holding a grandbaby. Then they were in a bar. There were a handful of pictures of Edward. Some where he was smiling, others where he was caught off guard, a couple of them he had his tongue sticking out, then he was sleeping in one, with a baby passed out on his chest. My face, my nose, my eyes, my lips, my smile, my hands, my skinny legs, my tiny ankles, my broad shoulders—me, him, me, him, me, him. "Bingo," I said.

Over the years there were many moments when I would be some-where, and I would glance across the room and I would see a person who looked like me. Often, the individual was a man—sometimes older than me, sometimes around my age—and I would wonder if I could be related to him in some way. A cousin? An uncle? A brother? A father? I might think he and I had the same nose or we were built the same and I would wonder—do I belong to that person?

If I had ever passed Edward Schneyder on the streets of Des Moines and looked up to see him passing me, I would have never guessed. I would have known immediately. That is how much we looked alike. This wasn't a "Maybe this could be my father?" It was an instant connection. In less than a second I knew: "I came from him."

Amy wasn't so sure. She ranked each man in her notebook and gave them a percentage of probability:

4. Bill 1%

3. Don 4%

2. Wayne 10%

1. Edward 85%

Our girls hovered over our shoulders as we passed photos of each man back and forth. Catey would see something in one that Rosie saw in another.

"It's one of these four brothers," Amy told them. "I don't think it's that one," she pointed to Bill. "I think it's down to these three."

Rosie grinned. "This is so exciting! It's like the movie *Mamma Mia!*"

Amy typed Louisa's name into Facebook and her account popped up. We looked at the profile picture of my DNA match. She was a slender lady, blond hair, glasses, pink lipstick, wearing a sleeveless blouse, and a gold necklace. She was holding a glass of wine and had a great smile.

"That's your aunt," Amy said. "And those are your grandparents." She waved the mouse over the pictures of George and Pauline. "At least you know that much."

I nodded and glanced at the clock. It was 9:37am. It felt like hours had passed but in reality, it had taken us about fifteen minutes to get this far.

"You come from the Sh-nay-der family," she said, trying to pronounce Schneyder. "Not as easy as Smith. But, it does begin with an S."

"Yeah, it does." I nodded. "I think it's pronounced Sh-nigh-der." I gave the name a whirl.

I sat back and watched as Amy continued to type names into Facebook. She would point to a profile picture and say things like, "That's an aunt." Or, "Look at this one! He has your nose! And so does he!" I definitely had the Sh-nay-der nose. "Do you see Catey in this one? God, you look like these people. Rosie looks like these people. Jill looks like these people." The girls all agreed.

I couldn't keep up with the names and faces. It was all a blur. I didn't know any of these people and yet here I was, stalking them, gawking in wonder at the resemblances to these strangers who were my blood. Rosie had plugged in Pandora on the TV and I heard the familiar notes of ABBA's *Mamma Mia* filling the living room.

Quietly, I picked up my phone and clicked on my Facebook app. I typed in "Louisa Schmidt" and brought up her profile picture. It said she lived in Grapevine, Washington. Amy was right, she must have moved. It also said she was from Lawrence, Iowa. She looked friendly and happy but everyone looks friendly and happy on Facebook. Still, she was my DNA match and in that moment, she was the one person that I felt connected with. "Hello, Louisa," I whispered.

EIGHT

The décor in our home consists heavily of photos of our combined families. We have a large mantel packed full of pictures and the wall against the staircase has classic photos following you up and down, a mix of Amy's side, my side, and our girls. Scattered around the living room are pictures of my grandmothers, a young version of my Grandma Peterson and an even younger one of my Grandma Lang. On our mantel, we have a photo of both my Grandma and Grandpa Lang. I love looking up from a hard workday and seeing my grandparents smiling down on me. With them gone, it's comforting having them still visible in my life.

AUGUST 1994

It had been over a year since I had talked with my mother about my biological father and I knew then that if I wanted to know more, I would have to talk to my grandparents. Every time I thought I might muster up the courage, I chickened out.

It was an odd thing to want to know something that was so important and intimately mine and, yet, I was scared to talk to my family about it. The thought of breaching the subject made me ill. What if I upset them? What if they got angry with me?

The only reason I felt that way was because of how the subject had been handled my entire life. I had been conditioned to be afraid to talk about it. Even this time, I considered backing out, thinking that this would be too much for my grandparents to relive. But I knew time wasn't on any of our sides and if I didn't ask, they would never make the first move. So, I pushed.

I sat down at my grandparents' kitchen table and fidgeted with an old plastic placemat. I pushed the white ceramic salt and pepper shakers away from me and then rearranged them until they were straight. My grandma, like my mom, was short with dark hair and dark eyes. She held a lot of weight in her middle but she was energetic, making sure everyone who came to visit always had something to eat or drink. She poured all of us a cup of coffee and settled across the table, next to my grandfather. Grandpa Lang was average height and was thin. He was balding, with a large nose. He was a very proud German, who often talked about his ancestors and was protective of their reputation. Grandpa Lang often praised the country he was from ... and he also refused to believe the Holocaust ever happened.

In secret, the grandkids referred to my grandfather as "Grumpa" because he was like a regular grandpa, only grumpier. He could love you up one minute and then curse you out the next. You didn't want to cross him, even in his old age. My grandfather was around seventy when this conversation occurred but in my mind, he always seemed much older. My grandma was nine years his junior, in her early sixties.

I had phoned my grandparents a couple of days before and told them I had some questions about my biological father so this table meeting between us was expected and to my pleasant surprise, they were not only open to the discussion, they were also thoughtful with their answers.

"I was wondering what you guys remember about my biological father," I began.

My grandmother started first. "Honestly, not much." She paused. "We knew Diane was seeing somebody but we didn't think it was very serious. All we knew was there was a boy coming over to pick her up and take her out."

"So he came to your house?"

"Our old house," my grandma nodded. When my grandparents retired, they sold the house they had lived in for thirty years and bought a mobile home.

"Did you meet him?"

They exchanged a look. My grandma shook her head. "Not really. We saw him walk up the driveway and he knocked on the door. Your mom was out the door pretty fast. We never shook his hand or anything."

I nodded. "Was he driving a motorcycle?"

My grandma took a moment to think. "I don't remember what he drove."

"I don't think I would have let your mother leave on a motorcycle," Grandpa chimed in. "But I don't remember what he drove, either."

Okay, I breathed. Let's try a simple question. "Do you remember his name?"

They both shook their heads. "We never formally met him." Grandma repeated.

Disappointing. "What did he look like?"

They talked over each other, Grandma then Grandpa. "Nice looking." "Tall." "Blond hair." "Or maybe more like a light brown." "Nice looking." "Real nice looking." "Looked like you." They both agreed on that one.

"I always thought you had my nose," Grandpa said. "This big ol' German honker but the older you got I realized that wasn't my nose. You got his."

"So..." I wrote their answers down in Amy's notebook. "What

did you guys do when Mom told you she was pregnant? Didn't you want to know who was responsible?"

"Well," my grandmother thought, "After she told him—"

"So Mom did tell him?" I interrupted.

Grandma nodded. "He called and she told him over the phone. He said he was coming over."

"Son of a bitch never showed up." Grandpa hit the table with his fist. "Couldn't face us! Couldn't face her! Ooh!"

I nodded. Grandpa seemed to be still holding on to some anger. "You guys didn't press her for more information?"

Grandma Lang shook her head. "It was a different time back then." She said it like this was a good reason why no one had any information about this man. They both acted like it was no big deal that they didn't know his identity. This was hard for me to grasp. Even at that time in my life, I knew if I were a father and my teenage daughter came home and told me that she was pregnant, my first question would be "Whose is it?" I would want names, addresses, phone numbers, parents' names, work numbers, Social Security numbers, library cards... I would ask questions. From what my grandparents were saying, it was like they hadn't asked any questions at all.

"I should've asked him his name when he came back," Grandpa quietly said.

"What do you mean? When he came back?"

Again, they exchanged looks. "When you were about four or five, he came back looking for you," my grandfather said, like this was old information.

"He did?"

"Yeah, he came to the house —"

"Our old house," Grandma nodded.

"And he knocked on the door —"

"I thought he was a salesman," Grandma interjected.

Grandpa cleared his throat. "He asked if Diane still lived there and I said 'No, she had moved out.' He mentioned he was passing through for work and he asked if Diane ever had the baby. I kind of looked at him funny and I realized, Oh my—this is Michael's father."

"I was so scared," my grandma said.

Grandpa folded his arms across his chest. "I started yelling at him. I told him to get off my doorstep and never come back! I said 'The little boy already has a father!' I chased him halfway down the driveway and said he didn't need to worry about anything because we had everything under control and he didn't have to show his face again! He got in his car and peeled outta there."

Grandma looked down at her hands, her thumbs chased one another. She was nervous. "I called Diane and told her 'Mikey's father was just here. He's come back for Mikey.' We were all so scared that he was going to try and take you away from us."

Scared was a word that I would include on a shortlist to describe both of my grandparents. Kind. Loving. Scared. Gullible. While my grandfather didn't believe that the Holocaust had ever happened, my grandmother truly believed that if she bought enough magazines, Ed McMahon would certainly show up on her doorstep to tell her that she had won Publisher's Clearing House.

"Do you recall what he was driving when he showed up that day?"

They shook their heads.

"Was his license plate from Iowa? Do you remember the county?"

My grandfather sighed. "I wouldn't have noticed anything like that. I just wanted him to go away."

I nodded. "Are you sure it was him?"

"Yeah," he said, glancing at Grandma. "He looked just like you," they said in unison.

"Thinner. More muscular," Grandma added. "Your face is more . . .

round."

Ah, yes, I was fatter than he was. Got it.

"I don't think I would have even remembered what he looked like if we only met him the one time but, the day he came back ..." she trailed off for a second and then nodded. "We got a good look at him that day."

We were all quiet. The disappointment I felt was palpable. On one hand, this was an interesting piece to my puzzle: He did know and he came back asking about me. On the other hand, none of the information they gave me helped my mission to find this mystery man.

My grandfather let out a deep sigh. "I shouldn't have chased him away that day. I should have invited him inside. I should have done it for you." He looked at me with mournful, sincere eyes. "At the very least, I should have got his name."

NINE

Edward Schneyder. I typed his name into Google. Address, telephone number, all the places he had lived, known relatives. He had a LinkedIn account, which listed him as retired. There was a document from Iowa Courts where he was called as a material witness in a trial involving his oldest son. I Googled his sons. Each one had a Facebook page. They all looked like me, in one way or another.

I walked by Amy, who was in the living room with her laptop open and her notebook next to it. "Edward is retired."

"Yeah, I saw that. LinkedIn."

I stared at my phone. "Looks like his oldest son has had a couple of run-ins with the law."

"Yeah, he definitely has a checkered past." Amy continued to type and then she turned her laptop toward me—Iowa Courts online for Adam Schneyder. It was two pages long of drug charges, assault, bad checks, and forgery.

"Oh."

Amy twirled the laptop back to her. "And then..." she typed and turned the laptop my way. "You have the middle brother, Mark. He's a police officer in Lawrence."

"What?" I scrolled through the screen. "So the oldest is a criminal and the middle one is the police?"

"Looks that way."

"Well, that sounds like that could cause some stress." The only pictures I had seen of the family together was at a wedding and they were all smiling. "What about the youngest?" Edward and his wife Bev had three sons.

"Kevin." Amy typed in his name. "He works at a factory and he's married. He just became a dad a couple of years ago. He seems like a regular guy. They live in Dubuque."

I nodded. Dubuque was a three-hour drive from us. Close enough to make contact.

"I'm ninety-nine percent sure Edward is my father," I told her.

Amy shrugged. "I don't know. It could be Wayne. It could be Don. I don't think it's Bill." We found a picture on Ancestry of all ten of the kids. One of their cousins had posted it. Of all the brothers, I looked the least like Bill. "I can't find if any of them ever lived in Des Moines. It seems like all four of them have lived around the Lawrence area their whole life."

Lawrence, Iowa. I had never been. When I first heard that they were from Lawrence, I immediately knew two things about the town:

First, twelve years earlier the town was flooded. Iowa is known for having floods but this was an incredibly destructive flood. The water destroyed one hundred homes and people were killed. It was all over the news. It had been devastating. I remember the amazing thing about Lawrence wasn't the flood but how resilient the residents had been. They worked together and rebuilt the town. The high school was reconstructed in three months and was running at full speed when fall classes commenced. Grocery stores were built, new homes were designed. There was no rest for the weary. The people of Lawrence were mighty, they persevered, they were strong.

The second thing I knew about Lawrence was it was small. Population: Two thousand.

"My high school had twenty-one hundred students in one building," Amy commented. I nodded. Mine had about a thousand.

I figured Lawrence was just small enough that everyone knew what was going on in everyone else's business. A blessing and a curse. I'm sure for a family that had lived there for over sixty years, they were well known and both equally loved and disliked.

I had to Google Lawrence on the map. It was just a small blip. As I dug deeper, I noticed there wasn't even any interesting landmarks or points of interest located there. It actually looked like a boring place to live.

I checked the driving directions and saw that it was almost a three hour drive from our house.

It had been four days since we discovered the Schneyders. I checked Ancestry and Louisa still had not signed on since September 2016. I didn't know how Ancestry worked as far as notifying people that they had a new match. Since joining six weeks before, I had received an email from them about every other day. *"Michael, there are new hints in your tree . . ."* Hints were little green leaves that you clicked on and Ancestry gave you all the information it had gathered on your long-lost relative. Every day new information was pouring into their databases so every other day, there was a new hint on some person who lived in 1832. As for today, I had no idea if Ancestry had sent an email containing my existence in Johnston, Iowa, all the way up to Louisa in Grapevine, Washington.

My days were preoccupied with typing the names of these four men into Facebook. I didn't search much further than that. I kept coming back to Edward over and over again. Amy, on the other hand, was a bloodhound, sniffing through the Facebooks' of all my aunts, uncles, cousins, and second cousins. She had started a family tree by hand, working through George and Pauline's own siblings, Googling and researching. She would often stop and show me a picture of a cousin or a great grandparent and she would comment about how much I looked like the family and how this girl looked like Rosie or this one looked like Jillian. It was undeniable.

"This one teaches Spanish. She's your first cousin...or your half-sister. Her name is Tara. And this one is named Michael, just like you! He's your cousin...or your half-brother. Probably your cousin, though." Amy's sleuthing made me both appreciative and annoyed at her. On the fifth day, I lost my shit.

"Okay, George and Pauline—you know, your grandparents—they had ten kids. From there those people have nine spouses and there are twenty-five grandkids—you would be number twenty-six. A lot of those people are married and here's a list of their spouses and many of those have their own families. You know how my family has a thing with the name Mary? These people are crazy about the name George. There are several Georges and Jerrys. Your grandma named all the girls with middle names that start with an A and all the boys with middle names that start with an M." Amy showed me the family tree that she had mapped out. It was a blur of lines leading to names leading to more lines and more names.

"What am I supposed to do with this?" I asked her. "I don't know any of these people! I don't know any of these names! I can't follow who belongs to who and where they fall in the family tree! You talk about people and I have no idea who you are talking about! Yes, I look like Jerry and Edward and Don and Ramona and Roland and I get it! These are my people! I have their nose! I like beer! And so does the other Michael! But I don't know him! I don't know any of them! I can't remember any of the shit you're telling me because I don't understand where I fit in with this family!" I took a breath. "There's so many of them. That's a lot of names and a lot of faces and noses. It's overwhelming."

To her credit, Amy shut her laptop and gave me her full, undivided attention. "Are you done?" she asked.

"No!" I yelled but didn't say anything else.

"First," Amy pointed to her notebook, "There are no Ramonas or Rolands." She smiled at me. "I know, this is a big family —"

"I have two cousins on my mom's side!" I yelled, suddenly remembering that I wasn't done. "Two! I have five cousins on my dad's side! That's it! I have seven cousins total!"

Amy nodded. "Now you have around twenty-five more, minus your siblings."

"I can't wrap my head around that!" I shouted. "You don't get it! That's a lot of people!"

"Well, I have thirty-nine cousins," Amy said.

I wanted to shake her. "Good for you! You win! You win! Your family is bigger than mine!" I yelled. "You get the prize!"

Amy burst out laughing. "I'm not pointing that out because we're in competition. I'm reminding you because my family has been preparing you for these people since we got married." She smiled. "Do you know all my aunts and uncles names?"

"Yes," I grudgingly replied.

"Do you know most of my cousins?"

"Yeah."

"If you passed my cousin Terri Jo on the street, would you recognize her and go up and shake her hand?"

"No," I said. "I would hug her."

Amy paused. "You are so loved by my family. My cousins think you're more fun than I am."

"That's because I *am* more fun than you."

Amy tapped the notebook. "This is a big family, but they're manageable. It may feel overwhelming right now but there are some really interesting people in this group."

I placed my hand over Amy's. "Okay, but I'm still absorbing

everything that's happened. I can only take one person at a time and you know who I'm concentrated on?" I flicked my fingers up. "Don, Bill, Edward, and Wayne. That's as far as my brain can go right now."

Amy nodded. "Alright," she agreed. "But eventually you have to move forward through the rest of these people. I don't want to see you get stuck on four guys."

"I won't," I took a cleansing breath. "I know this is a big family and I hope that at least one of them will want to know me . . . want to know us. If we can get just one person who is interested in knowing us, that will be one more person in our lives to love. It will be our bonus person."

Amy smiled. "I like that. A bonus. Someone we didn't know could even exist last week. A new family member. Everyone can use more family. Everyone needs more love in their life."

It felt good to know that we were getting back on the same page, slowing our pace down. "First I need to figure out which of these guys is my bio-dad," I said. "And I'm not going to get stuck. I know what I have to do next."

"What's that?" Amy asked.

"I need to write Louisa." I rubbed the top of my head. This could go very, very bad. "Hopefully I won't be the second flood that takes out Lawrence."

TEN

Dear Louisa,

My name is Michael Blair. I'm reaching out to you because recently, I completed a DNA kit on Ancestry.com and according to our DNA results, you and I have virtually a 100% match that we are either grandmother/ grandson, half-siblings, or aunt/nephew. Given our age difference, I am under the assumption that you most likely may be my biological aunt.

My birthday is February 18, 1972. I was born in Des Moines, Iowa. My mother's name was Diane Lang, now Diane Blair. My mother explained to me when I was 18 that the father who raised me was not my biological father. No other information has been offered.

My best guess would be that I was conceived in May/June of 1971 and it most likely occurred in Des Moines.

After receiving my DNA results on Ancestry, I believe that my biological father could possibly be a brother to you.

I realize this may be a lot for you to process. I have been searching for my biological father for many years with very little to work with. Without the new DNA technology, my search has been close to impossible. While this may be surprising, I am hopeful that you will be able to help me.

If you're open to the idea, I would very much appreciate a phone conversation when it's convenient for you.

Best regards,

Michael Blair

I added my email address and phone number. And, without hesitation, I pressed send.

I sent the email via Ancestry's website. There was a messaging option, but once again, I did not know how this worked. Would Louisa get a notification in her personal email that someone had sent her a message or would she have to log on to the site to see that she had a message waiting for her? I tried Googling my questions but did not get much except it depended on how each individual set up their account. All I could do was wait.

That night we went to dinner with our neighbors. Five couples sitting at a large table, chatter ranging from football games to upcoming school concerts. The biggest conversation that night was my weighted AncestryDNA results.

When I was in high school and suspected my dad was not my biological dad, I confided my suspicions to my friends. That day when my mother stopped vacuuming long enough to tell me that my assumptions were true, one of the first things I did was tell my friends that I was right. This revelation of mystery was something I never kept secret. I have told co-workers throughout the years, all of Amy's family knew, all of her friends knew. It wasn't information that I opened with but as my relationships with people grew, talk of family and childhood came up and I was honest about my journey. What I learned from this was that I was not alone. Along the way, I ran into many people who were in the same boat as myself, not knowing who their bio-father was or that they were completely adopted. I felt a kinship to these people and talked at length with them about the measures they took to find answers to their own personal journeys.

Our neighbors knew the night of the Super Bowl. Amy and I couldn't hide what we had just discovered and they were all encouraging to us, each one looking at pictures of Edward versus Wayne and asking to see pictures of possible sibling matches to compare.

"I've never seen that last name before," our neighbor Justin commented. "Have you ever seen or heard of anyone having that last name before?"

I shook my head. "No. We're not even sure how to pronounce it."

Justin attempted it. "I think it's Sk-nay-der."

His guess was as good as mine. I spent several minutes staring at the name and so far I felt no connection to it. I had doodled the name on a piece of paper. *Schneyder. Michael Schneyder. Michael Lee Schneyder.* It didn't feel right. Not even a little bit. Even if I didn't know how it was pronounced.

All of our neighbors hoped for the best end result—that I would find my bio-father and he would be open to a relationship with me.

"That is what you want, isn't it?" Our neighbor Kelly asked me.

"Of course it is," I replied. And that felt amazingly scary to admit. "But I'm keeping my expectations low."

We went home and spent the rest of the night refreshing my Ancestry page every hour. It didn't seem like Louisa had seen my message and it still showed her last login date as September 2016.

Four days went by and nothing changed. I was teetering on whether I needed to go a different route to contact Louisa. Her Facebook account, as well as her address and phone number, were glaring at me every time I plugged her name into Google.

FEBRUARY 14TH, 2017. VALENTINE'S DAY.

Amy was scheduled to have a hysterectomy.

"It was the only day in February that was open," she told me.

"I wonder why." I rolled my eyes.

We arrived at the hospital and the staff swarmed around her, prepping her for the surgery. As a nurse, Amy knew a lot of what to expect. The transporter came in to get her. "Okay," the anesthesiologist popped his head behind the curtain, "we're going to head down to the operating room now."

As they were wheeling her away, Amy shoved the anesthesiologist to the side and yelled at me, "If Louisa writes back while I'm under, be sure it's the first thing you tell me when I wake up! I hate that I might miss it!"

Yeah, we weren't excited at all.

Amy's surgery took longer than expected. I didn't see her for another four hours. She was admitted and had to stay overnight. I walked into her hospital room and saw two nurses and a nurse's aide hovered around her bed. Amy heard me enter over all the noise and her eyes landed on me. "Did Louisa write?"

I shook my head.

"Oh." Disappointment. She really did think that while she was sleeping, contact was going to happen. She was kind of right.

"While you were under, I got a new match. I have a new second cousin."

"You do?" Amy shooed away the nurses, assuring them that she did not need any pain medicine and that all she really wanted was the room service menu. Once alone, I pulled out my laptop.

"He already wrote me," I said.

"You're kidding!"

I shook my head and brought up Ancestry. "It's pretty short and sweet," I said. "His name is Jerry Wachtel." Another weird last name that I had never heard of before.

"Hi, Michael—I just received my DNA results and you are listed as a possible second cousin match to me. I have completed my family's genealogy and have created a master book. I have looked through this book and I don't see your name listed. Are you related to Wachtel, Schneyder, or Harrison? If you're interested, I would like to communicate more

with you."

"Wow," Amy laughed. "Well, Louisa hasn't written you back and this guy is open to talking to you. I think you should write him. But be vague."

I nodded. "I'm worried about how fast this news is traveling through the family. I don't want to scare anyone away."

"You can only control so much," Amy said. "And you're just going to keep matching to people on Ancestry. I think you should write Jerry. Be honest with him and be you. But be brief."

Dear Jerry,

Thanks for writing! Yes, I would be open to communicating with you. I was raised by my biological mother and was adopted by my father. I do not know the identity of my biological father and he is someone whom I have searched for now for many years. I, too, just received my AncestryDNA results. I have matched closely with a woman named Louisa Schmidt. At this time, I am presuming that Louisa would be my aunt. I reached out to her about a week ago but haven't heard back yet. Are you in contact with Louisa?

All my best,

   Michael Blair

Jerry wrote back within two hours.

Dear Michael,

Louisa is my cousin, my mom and her mom were sisters. She has several brothers, as there was ten children. Louisa is on Facebook. She is a very nice lady."

   Best regards — Jerry

I read his response to Amy. "Is that it?"

"That's it." I shrugged.

Within that breath, I had another message from Jerry.

Dear Michael,

I can send you the PDF of the file I created on our family's genealogy.

May I email it to you?

Amy smiled. "*Our* family. Look at the big balls on Jerry."

Dear Jerry,

Of course! I would love to look at it!

By the time Amy had her dinner, I had the email from Jerry. The PDF on his family history was three hundred pages long. "How am I going to navigate through this?" There was a section on the Schneyders. All of them. I guessed there were two hundred of them listed. My phone pinged. "I just got a friend request on Facebook from Jerry Wachtel."

Amy smiled as she ate her vanilla pudding.

I immediately responded: Confirm.

I went out to Ancestry and clicked on my messages. I couldn't tell if Louisa had read my email, but then I noticed that there wasn't any indication that Jerry had read any either, when he obviously had.

I clicked on Louisa's name. Last Logged In: Today.

I looked at Amy. My heart skipped a beat. "Shit just got real."

ELEVEN

Conversing with Jerry went on for a week. He openly commented on things that I posted on Facebook and sometimes worried me that one of my family members was going to pick up on things he was saying and figure out what I was doing. But I also appreciated how transparent he was and in some ways, it gave me comfort knowing that there was a blood relative—even as distant as a second cousin—who acknowledged me as his family.

If none of them ever accepted me, Jerry was there. In that delicate week, for me, Jerry was a life preserver.

FEBRUARY 18, 2017

Amy, the girls, and I celebrated my forty-fifth birthday. I asked for a low-key day. For once in her life, Amy obliged. Four days later, on the 22nd, Jerry sent me a private message through Facebook: *Louisa is waiting for your call. She is a very nice and understanding person.* Then he included her phone number.

I hurried upstairs and read Amy the message. "I'm not going to call this lady out of the blue. I wouldn't want someone to cold call me. What am I supposed to do?"

Amy, who was not typically a composed person, seemed to have moments of calm when I needed it. "Sit down and write her on Ancestry again. Tell her you and Jerry have been in contact and he has mentioned she's open to a conversation. See if she's available this week."

We had noticed that Louisa had logged on to her Ancestry account every day that week. I was hopeful that I would hear from her, but so far, there was nothing but crickets. I clicked on the Ancestry app.

Dear Louisa,

Good morning. I hope that you have had time to absorb my first message. I have been in contact with Jerry Wachtel, who matched me as a second cousin. He has informed me that he has been in contact with you and that you are open to a phone conversation. I was wondering if this week would work sometime? I am a professor at DMACC, the local community college, and am available tonight and tomorrow evening. I am sure I can also carve out some free time this weekend.

Looking forward to hearing from you,

Michael

Send.

I never hesitated on the send. If I gave myself the chance to overthink it, the send key would never get pressed.

I hoped my message didn't sound too pushy or too desperate. "Carve out some free time" really meant "I will rearrange anything that I have going on to be sure I am available for your phone call." Of course, that would sound too pathetic so I chose to craft my words better.

Two hours later, I had my first message from Louisa:

Hi, Michael,

I would welcome a call from you. I am retired from a community college as well and currently live in Grapevine, WA. My husband Henry and I babysit our twin granddaughters during the day but tonight I will have some free time. I would be happy to have a phone conversation with you around 8:00pm your time. Would that work for you?

Louisa.

I wrote back:

Hi, Louisa!

Yes, that would be perfect!

And she responded with her phone number.

The thought of calling Louisa made me sick to my stomach. Everything inside of me was zinging, my senses were on high alert, I felt like my heart was going to explode out of my chest.

I asked Amy to sit next to me while I dialed Louisa's number and then after she answered, I wanted to be alone. I wrote the number down in Amy's notebook, under five questions that we had thought to ask Louisa. The last question was Louisa's thoughts on the identity of my biological father—did she already know or was there a brother she suspected? Then Amy had written: Edward? And circled his name so I wouldn't forget to ask specifically about him.

"Did you check the number to be sure it's correct?"

"It's the right number," I snapped.

"Sometimes, when you get nervous, your dyslexia kicks in," Amy pointed out.

I frowned. "I wrote down the right number, Amy."

I dialed the number twice. It didn't go through.

Amy sighed. I ignored her and popped up Facebook to recheck the digits Jerry had sent to me. I had two numbers mixed up. I corrected my error but paused. "I have a private message from a lady named Carolyn Schneyder Kriegel," I said. I clicked and read it to Amy.

Hi, Michael this is Carolyn Schneyder Kriegel. I am sitting with Jerry Wachtel's sister. Louisa Schmidt is my sister. If you would like to talk, you can reach me at . . .

My heart, which was already beating ten beats faster than normal, kicked up a notch. "Oh, my God. All these people are finding out. It's spreading."

Amy was quiet for a couple of seconds. "You can only control what you have in front of you. Don't worry about Carolyn right now—concentrate on Louisa." She tapped the notebook. "Don't get sidetracked. Call this one."

"Okay. Right." I tucked the message from Carolyn—*Aunt Carolyn*—away and took a breath. I pushed the buttons on my phone and pressed it to my ear. It rang three times before Louisa answered. Her voice was crisp, clear, and confident. Everything mine was not.

"Hello, Michael," she said.

In my peripheral vision, I saw Amy's face break out into a grin. We made brief eye contact. Amy nodded, got up, and walked out of our bedroom.

"Hi, Louisa," I said. My voice shook. I hoped she didn't notice. My left hand started doodling all over the notebook. *Louisa. Louisa Schmidt. Schneyder. Edward. Schneyder. Michael Schneyder . . .*

Our conversation started slow, like a roller coaster starting off low and slow and building up higher. We talked about the DNA results and Ancestry. Louisa confirmed with me that she had been a part of Ancestry for many years and she had great interest in researching her family tree.

"The Schneyder family has deep roots in Germany. There is actually a brother who stayed behind and his family still farms the original Schneyder land. I have visited there."

Schneyder. Louisa pronounced it Sk-need-er. She gave me a brief background on herself. She was married, had one son who was in his thirties and he was married and had twin daughters. Louisa was a teacher and taught community college, her son was a Professor of English Studies at a college in Washington. "Of course, I suppose that gene has been passed down through the years to many of us. My mother was a teacher."

I held my breath. Seriously, this must be where I got my desire to teach! As Louisa talked, I was noting many similarities between myself and this new family. I told Louisa about matching to Jerry and that he and I had been conversing through Facebook. I told her about getting the message from Carolyn just seconds before I called. That news seemed to interest Louisa. "Hmmm, she did? Okay, well, I guess that means this news is traveling faster than even I expected."

Then, she got down to the nitty-gritty.

"When I got your email, I was very surprised. As far as I was aware, none of my brothers have fathered any additional children, besides the ones that they have now. So your message took me off guard. I felt I needed to talk to one of my siblings to help me muddle through this. In 1971, I wasn't at home. I'm number-three of ten kids and by that time, I was away at college and caught up in my own drama, and so my recollection of what was happening back home isn't the best."

I nodded. "Okay. I understand that."

"So I called one of my sisters who still lives in the area. She is part of the younger kids and was living at home during that time. I explained your situation and read her your email. After some back and forth, she felt strongly that your father was our brother Wayne. So I called and talked with him. He immediately denied it and said it wasn't him. He said in 1971, he was eighteen and was graduating from high school and that he hadn't been to Des Moines. He was adamant it wasn't him."

"Sure," I said. I crossed Wayne off the list.

"So I made another phone call to another brother that my sister and I thought could be your father. I read him your email and, well, he denied it. He said No, no, no . . . that it wasn't him, either . . . even though he was working and living in Des Moines in 1971. So after talking with him, I said, 'If you aren't this man's father, then I'm hanging up with you and calling our brother Bill to ask him.' Well, then my brother said, 'Wait a minute. Don't call Bill. There was a girl.' But he also followed that up with that he really didn't think there was any way that you could be his."

I crossed Bill's name off the list. That left me with two possibilities, Don and Edward. I remembered that Don was twenty-five in 1971 and he had already been married for two years. My eyes skipped over his name and landed on Edward, which Amy had circled. I laughed lightly at Louisa's story to keep the air between us as easy as possible. "Would that brother happen to be Edward?" I asked.

Louisa had been careful with her words and I don't think she would have named him if I hadn't asked, but since I did, she cleared her throat. "Yes, that's right. My brother Edward."

When I hung up the phone, Amy was bouncing on the other side of the door, waiting to hear how the conversation went. "Well," I said, "eighteen days since we found these people and we are still pronouncing their name wrong. It's Sk-need-er."

"Sk-need-er? Seriously? Michael Schneyder. Amy Schneyder." She made a face. "Please don't make me change my name. I don't want to be Amy Schneyder."

I grinned. The name did sound alien. "I won't. I promise."

"You spoke to your first biological relative." Amy hugged me. I hugged her back and let myself breathe for a minute. I could feel my heart beating against Amy's chest. The whoosh of my blood was electrified as it pumped through my veins. My blood. Lang blood, Schneyder blood. I closed my eyes and just let the moment be. I was excited and scared and relieved all at the same time. I let Amy go and locked eyes with her. "I was right. It's Edward."

TWELVE

The next few days felt like I was dreaming. I ran the conversation Louisa and I had over and over in my head. I looked back on my notes. I thought of more questions that I wanted to ask her but I was nervous to overstep my boundaries. I was absorbing new information about this huge family and she was absorbing new information about me. This couldn't be easy for her. I found my own thoughts were consumed of Edward and how he was possibly handling things. I wondered if he was freaking out in anticipation of what my next step would be.

I wondered that myself.

I asked Amy not to mention the Schneyders for a few days. I needed a break from all of it and I was falling behind on my grading. For the most part, she stayed quiet. It was when I would break my own rule and bring up something that she would then talk about something she had uncovered or connections she had put together. One of those things was the day following my phone call with Louisa was Edward's 65th birthday.

"It was? Aw, man." I felt bad about that. Here was a guy probably looking forward to a milestone birthday, maybe had plans to go out with his family and friends, and now he has this on his mind? I wondered if he was talking to anyone about me or if he was keeping things secret.

"And then," Amy pulled up her laptop and turned it toward me, "there's this." She typed in Edward's oldest son into Google and an arrest popped up. He had been taken in on a warrant and was now in a county jail. From the looks of it, several counties were requesting him to serve time in their jail. He was going to be away for a few months. Amy pointed to the date: he had been arrested on Edward's birthday.

"Son of a bitch," I whispered. Not only did Edward have to deal with his oldest son's legal problems, he also had to deal with the fact that a surprise son was suddenly in the picture. All of this happening on his birthday. Talk about bad timing.

"What are you going to do?" Amy asked.

"I didn't come this far just to come this far," I said.

I knew this was not exactly the moment I had waited for. In my mind, I had pictured this happening to a man who was ready for the news or a man who was surprised by the information but intrigued to know who his son was. For twenty-five years I had envisioned the different ways to tell him. I hadn't thought it would come in a moment where he was experiencing such personal stress. But from the online courts, it looked like this kind of worry was something the family was used to and a big part of my end game was to contact my birth father. If I waited, something else could come along. That's how life worked, you wait, you lose. And I was ready.

How was never the question. I wasn't going to cold call Edward. "Hey, guess who?" I also had no intentions of showing up at his doorstep with a bottle of Jack and two glasses. I was going to write him a letter. I did briefly consider designing a card announcing "It's a Boy!" but I thought he may not find the humor in that. It took me a few days of planning and editing to get my words right.

Dear Edward,

My name is Michael Lee Blair. Recently I completed a DNA kit on Ancestry.com and I have discovered that Louisa Schmidt is my biological aunt and Jerry Wachtel is my second cousin. I understand that Louisa has been in contact and shared this information with you. I strongly believe you would be my biological father.

My birthday is February 18, 1972 and I was born in Des Moines, Iowa. My mother's name was Diane Lang, now Diane Blair. My mother explained to me when I was 18 that the father who raised me was not my biological father (although I was able to determine this when I was much younger). My mother and I have had several conversations about my origins throughout the years. It has never ended well. I've always been left with more questions than answers. Other than this topic, my mother and I have a good relationship; however, she does not know that I am currently on this journey.

Through a lot of soul-searching over the years and especially in the past few weeks I have come to terms that what has happened in the past doesn't matter. Life happens. Life happened to me, and it's been a good one so far.

I've been married for 23 years to my wife Amy, we have three girls: Roslyn (19), Catherine (13) and Jillian (12). My career as a Graphic Designer and as a Professor of Design at Des Moines Area Community College has taught me that this world is full of challenges and unexpected surprises. Keeping an open mind and heart are imperative to dealing with what life throws at us.

I'm not looking for an explanation about what has happened in the past and I hold no animosity toward you. Nor do I want to upset or disrupt lives. Just knowing that you're in the world has given me peace of mind and a relief I've been seeking for more than thirty years. I would *be open to connecting with you in the future if you're interested. If you feel the same, please feel free to contact me and we can make arrangements to meet.*

Hope to hear from you soon,

Michael Blair

I added my contact information and stuffed the letter into an addressed envelope. I looked for a stamp before I left for work that Monday but Amy said she had just used the last one so I took the letter with me. My morning flew by and at lunchtime, I locked my office and headed out to Hy-Vee, our local grocery store, to grab a five-dollar pizza. I took the letter in and walked up to customer service.

"I need to mail this," I said. "Is there any way I can purchase just one stamp?"

"Sure," a cheery lady said. She fumbled around in small cubby holes under the counter. "Here we go." She took the letter from my hand and placed it snuggly in front of her. "You're in luck—this is the last Valentine's Day stamp I have left!"

Then I watched in horror as she pressed a great big heart stamp with the word LOVE written in script across it. I heard the word "NOOOOOOO!" scream in my head as she opened the mailbox behind her and with a flick of her wrist—she tossed the letter in. "Have a great day." She smiled.

I walked away. I mean, I don't know how I walked away because I couldn't feel my legs, but somehow I walked away. And I hoped. I hoped he would respond to my letter because I didn't want this to be our first and last interaction. Twenty-five years is a long time to wait for someone who you never thought you would have the chance to find and, for the first time, I felt like I was close.

My stomach twisted. I skipped the pizza and opted for the soup instead. I felt like I had just sent a bomb through the mail.

THIRTEEN

I sent my letter to Edward on Monday and that Friday, Amy and I went to a movie. Amy was still recovering from her hysterectomy and had some cabin fever. *Logan* was out in theaters and Amy was so desperate to leave our children that she agreed to see it. Side note: Marvel movies are the best and anyone who doesn't agree with me is wrong.

We headed out to FLIX Brewhouse, where we could grab a burger and a beer before the show. As we were eating, I checked my emails. There, waiting in my inbox, was a message from Louisa.

Hello Michael, My brother Edward called this morning and told me that he had received your letter. He has not, at this time, told his wife about your correspondence. So he asked me to act as an intermediary in the meantime. Before talking with his children and after talking with his wife, he would like to submit DNA for a paternity test. However, at the moment Bev's 90-year-old mother isn't doing well and another family crisis is emotionally draining for her. Edward feels that sharing your correspondence at this time might be overwhelming for her. He believes the crisis will be partially resolved within the next six weeks at which time he will share your correspondence with her.

As you can understand, Edward wants to be the one to tell Bev and is

conflicted about withholding your correspondence and keeping it secret
for even a week let alone six. I have assured him that, for my part, the
information will remain between the three of us. I can imagine that
waiting longer is very difficult for you. And I want to assure you that
Edward is sincere about following up with you. He asked that I email
you as soon as possible.

Louisa

I threw my phone at Amy and jammed my hands into my coat pockets. She stopped eating and read Louisa's note. "Michael," she said, "this is a good email. I know it's not exactly what you were hoping for but he's not telling you No. He's not blowing you off. This is a positive response. He just needs a few weeks and to be honest," she gently passed my phone back to me, "we could all use the break. Everything is happening so fast."

I understood what she meant. We had dragged all these years of waiting and chasing flimsy leads and crammed it into two weeks of nothing but fast-fast-fast. Sometimes the information was too much to absorb. It was overwhelming. For me. For Amy. For our girls. "I get that," I admitted. "I just want to know if it's him for sure. I want to know, like, *now*."

"I know you do. But you can give him six weeks. We don't know his side of the story yet. He's still taking this in."

I stared at the email and released a big breath. "Okay, I'll write Louisa back and tell her to let him know that I can wait." Which is what I did.

Amy finished her sandwich and I drank the last of my beer. I ordered another one and followed her into the movie theater. It was hard to concentrate on *Logan*, my mind preoccupied on Louisa and

Edward and now his wife, Bev. He hadn't told her. I was right—my news had been poorly timed. I wondered if Edward was sitting at his home in Lawrence, thinking about me. Had he hid my letter somewhere? Did he dig it out three times a day and reread it, trying to figure out clues, like I had done my whole life? Did he study my handwriting and try to get a feel for who I was? Did he look at the large, heart shaped love stamp and think *'Dude, what the hell?'*

The beer was working against me and I started to feel the pull of sleep. I knew it was a combination of the alcohol and being physically and emotionally exhausted. Two weeks of going at full speed ahead and suddenly a request for a six-week reprieve. I could rest.

I fell asleep midway through the movie and missed most of it until I woke up at the end, just in time to see Logan turn toward the young female character and acknowledge himself as the father the young girl had never known and, in return, she admitted that deep down inside, that she always knew she was his daughter.

They had a final, loving moment . . . then he died in her arms.

FOURTEEN

The baby scoop era occurred from 1940 to 1975. This was a time where young, single women found themselves pregnant and not having the means to support their babies. Their families would often send them away to an unwed mother's home to give birth and ultimately surrender their child for adoption. Some 300,000 American women gave birth and relinquished children during this time. Many of those babies were taken against their mother's wishes. Organizations such as Catholic Charities and the Salvation Army took these girls in, under the pretense that they would provide school and shelter for them, in exchange for their babies. After the women gave birth, many of the mothers would beg the nuns and social workers to let them keep their babies and in return, the social workers would explain to them that their family would not let the girl return to her home if she kept the baby. They would tell the new mother, "You agreed to live here and give them your baby. All these months, they have invested in you, provided schooling and housing. If you keep your baby, you will need to pay the balance of two thousand dollars before you walk out the door. Do you have the money?"

Many of these girls were forced to give up their children for adoption. They were told that they did this to themselves, they were the ones who had sex and now they had to pay for their sins. Words like "whores" and "sluts" were used to describe them. The girls were told that they were an embarrassment to their family, they were a problem that their family had to deal with, their actions were sins, and their babies were bastards. They were shamed because of their pregnancies. Adoption was the only way to make themselves clean again.

The would-be-fathers during the baby scoop era were basically off the hook. There would be the occasional boyfriend who would come forward and take responsibility for his actions, but for most girls, when she named the boy who had impregnated her, she was either not believed or when the boy was questioned, he denied it. There was no knowledge of DNA at this time and so girls could not prove paternity. This allowed young men to continue on with their lives, unscathed, without the shame the girls battled with, hanging over their heads. Boys progressed with their schooling, they graduated, they were able to have social lives, some went to the service, some to college, some went straight to work. Many of them never saw the girl again. They never knew if she had the baby and if she did, whether it was a boy or a girl. These girls became ghosts of memories for them, fading further and further from their mind.

The lack of DNA testing and the inability to prove paternity also gave the young men a scapegoat. "It's not mine." was a common line parents and social workers heard. But more than that, the fact that there was nothing in black-and-white to say that they were the fathers gave these young men the go-ahead to tell themselves that it couldn't be them. If they could believe it themselves that the girl must have been with another boy, that she was easy, that the dates didn't match up with how far along she was . . . then the young men could go on through their lives without the guilt. It was her problem, not theirs.

When my mother found out she was pregnant, in 1971, it was at the tail-end of the baby scoop era. Girls were beginning to find their voice. More and more unwed mothers were keeping their babies. As a society, people were understanding that removing babies from their mothers against their will was destroying families. The nuns and social workers had been wrong: these women didn't forget their babies, they weren't able to leave those nine months in the past and move on. Not without scars. Relinquishing their babies caused life-long suffering. Roe versus Wade wasn't legal until 1973 so a young girl, like my mother, finding out that she was "in trouble" now had two viable choices: adopt the baby out or keep it.

I can't imagine what it must have been like for a seventeen-year-old girl to go to her father and explain that she was pregnant with some guy's baby. A guy she didn't know. My grandfather must have been furious. My mother, not wanting to relive the shame he rained upon her, simply told me, "Grandpa made it difficult."

I know that my Grandma Lang would have been in my mom's corner. She wouldn't have wanted to give her first grandchild away. I am sure a big reason why my mom was able to keep me was because Grandma made it possible.

In 1994, after my grandparents told me their side of the story of meeting my biological father, I went back to my mother one more time and said to her, "I talked with Grandma and Grandpa about my bio-dad. They said he came back when I was around four or five. Why didn't you mention that?"

My mom was immediately defensive. "Why would you question your grandparents about this?"

"Because they were there."

"I told you everything I know."

"Except that he came back to check on me."

She was quiet.

"What do you know about that?"

My mother shrugged. "Grandma called and she was very upset.

She said your father had stopped by and that he and Grandpa got into a fight and Grandpa chased him away."

"When did this happen?"

My mom thought for a moment. "Craig and I were living in our apartment ... we didn't buy our house until you were five. So, you must have been four."

"1976, then?"

"I guess."

"And you guys were living in the apartment? The one behind Grandma's house?" I had a vague memory of living there. Before my parents married, they rented the upstairs apartment of a house, one street over from my grandparents. My bedroom was in a closet.

"Yeah."

I blinked. "All the guy had to do was drive around the block! He came looking for me and he could have thrown a rock and knocked out the kitchen window!" I was seething. "And you guys sent him away!"

"Don't yell at me!" my mother countered. "I didn't even know he was there until after he was gone!"

I took in a couple of breaths and closed my eyes. It took me a long minute but when I looked at her again, she was sitting on the sofa, a blank look on her face. "Why didn't you tell me that he had come back?"

"Because I didn't think you needed to know. What good is it going to do? What does it matter?"

"What does it matter?" I might have laughed if I wasn't so pissed. "It matters because there was a moment in time when this guy cared enough that he came back to check in on me. And nobody had the brains to ask him 'Hey, by the way, what's your name?' or 'You got a phone number?' I would think you would've wanted to sue him for child support or something."

"Believe me, if I knew who he was, I would have gotten child support!"

That, I believed. I grew up with parents who were always broke. We never had enough money. No family vacations, no brand-new cars, I wore secondhand clothes, sometimes I came home and the power had been shut off. I shook my head. "When I asked you before, you said you told me everything and then when I talked to Grandma and Grandpa, they said he came back. You knew that and you didn't tell me."

My mother didn't say anything, she didn't look at me. I knew reliving her pregnancy and her choice to keep me brought back waves of embarrassment for her. I was a shame baby. As much as she loved me, as much as she fought for me, she couldn't take away the stain that I didn't have a father. It was hard for me to understand how she was feeling and where she came from and, in return, it was hard for her to understand my point of view of not knowing.

I turned to leave the house when she said, "I was listening to Dr. Laura the other night and a lady called in. She said she had a son who didn't know that his stepfather wasn't his biological father. She didn't know the identity of his bio-dad and she felt guilty because she felt as though she was lying to her son about who his father was. Dr. Laura told her to never tell him and that the lady had given her son a father when she picked her husband. So, Dr. Laura thinks I did the right thing."

I couldn't believe my ears. I smiled but it was weak. It was important for my mom to think that she got it right. She hadn't been in the wrong. Not then, not now. "Well, if that lady takes Dr Laura's advice, it's only going to end poorly for her. You know what I think? Dr. Laura is a dipshit," And I walked out the door.

FIFTEEN

The stories we tell are uniquely ours. Over the years, digging through paperwork and questioning my family on what they remembered about my own origin, I have learned that everyone settles on a story in their mind and that story is true. To them. That doesn't mean it's the true story. What my mom remembered versus my grandparents versus my other family members is just a version of the truth. Time and circumstances have rewritten the stories of each of our lives. All of us think we know the truth about ourselves. In reality, it's just sort of the truth because the truth about the past is hard to pin down. A great chunk of all of our truths has been lost.

It had been forty-six years since I was conceived. That's a lot of time to pass. And for someone living in the quiet of a big secret, it gives them years of perfecting their own story, crafting it to tip the hand to their advantage, if ever that secret comes to bloom.

MARCH 11, 2017

The day after Amy and I saw *Logan*, we were all hanging out at home. It was a Saturday and the girls were bothering Amy about going to the mall and making plans for dinner. I was in the living room, working on a project for school.

At 3:30 that afternoon, twenty hours after agreeing to Louisa that I could wait Edward's requested six weeks, my phone rang. I looked at the caller ID. No name, just a phone number and under that, the words Lawrence, IA. I slid over the bar and answered, "Hello?"

"Michael?"

"Yes, that's me."

"Hi, Michael. This is Ed Schneyder." So much for six weeks. Edward and I already had something in common besides our good looks: apparently we both hated to wait.

I stood up from the sofa and loudly said, "Hi, Ed."

I have never seen Amy nor any of the girls quiet down so fast. It was record time. They turned and looked at me. I was already in motion, walking. "This is a surprise," I said.

"Yeah," Edward agreed. "I, uh, got your letter –"

"You got that, did you?" I opened the basement door and retreated downstairs to my office for more privacy.

"I did," Edward said. "So . . ." he hesitated. "How long have you known about me?"

This first question is the question I mostly play back in my mind, trying to reread the meaning. In the moment, I thought Edward was asking how long had I known about him being my biological father? In the months to come, I will question if what he was asking was more personal than I picked up on in the beginning.

"I just received my Ancestry results a couple of weeks ago and I was matched to Louisa." I picked up a pen and started doodling, my nervous energy finding an outlet.

"Okay, so, not long?"

"No."

This seemed to please him. Edward's conversation with me lasted about twenty minutes. He admitted that he had not yet told his wife and he was nervous to do so. "I don't know how she will handle this." The main purpose of the call was to find out who I had talked to since getting the results.

"Just Louisa and Jerry." I confided in him about Carolyn messaging me. He was not pleased that both Jerry and Carolyn knew. "I walk into the Dollar Store and I swear everyone is staring at me. I feel like they already know. People like to talk. Lawrence is a small town and information spreads fast. By the time someone hears news, they get it confused. Tomorrow people will be saying that I have a four-or five-year-old son, instead of forty-five."

I didn't miss the word son. "Jerry and I have had very minimal contact." I tried to ease his worry.

"Jerry hasn't lived in Lawrence for years," he told me. "But some of his siblings live around here and I don't know if he's told them. I really don't want my wife to hear about this secondhand I'm nervous that she will ... I-I can't think straight. The other day she told me we were going to go to meet some friends at Pat's and I thought she said Mass. I couldn't figure out why we would be going to church on a Friday night."

I wrote down "Mass" and briefly wondered if he and his wife were religious and if that was a good thing of not.

"Have you spoken to my sister Carolyn?" he asked.

"No," I replied. "I only got the one message from her on Facebook and I haven't had any further contact with her."

"Well, I would appreciate it if you wouldn't talk to her for now."

"Okay," I agreed. I could do that.

"I haven't spoken to her in eight years," he said. Then he added, "In fact, I haven't talked to any of my brothers or sisters in eight years."

That's odd, I thought. Especially since I had just received the email from Louisa yesterday where she stated she and Edward had spoken. "Really? Eight years?"

"Yeah," he said. "I'm not close with any of them. And Louisa ... well, she's more interested in our family who lived three hundred years ago than the ones who are actually alive today."

I didn't say anything except, "Huh. Okay."

"Does your wife know that you have been doing all this?" he asked.

"Absolutely," I said.

"And your kids? Do they know about me?"

I nodded. "They do. They have been my biggest supporters."

He was quiet. I could feel an invisible divide already. Here he was trying to keep me a secret from his family and I was doing the exact opposite, sharing everything with mine. It felt taut between us. "Listen, I want you to know that I don't remember your mother. I mean, there was this girl that I had an encounter with but I don't . . . I don't know how you could be here. We didn't . . . it wasn't . . ."

"It's okay," I said. "You don't have to explain."

"I don't think you're mine," Edward said.

"All right." I didn't want to scare him away. "DNA doesn't lie and the DNA says Louisa is my aunt—"

"Yeah, I know." He paused. "I mean, I lived in Des Moines in 1971. Me and four other guys from Lawrence rented a house there –"

"That's what my mom told me. She talked about that house," I interrupted.

Edward quieted. "She did?" Then, slowly, he asked, "Have you told your mother you found me?"

"No," I replied. "Not yet."

Edward didn't say anything. I wondered if he was writing down my answers just as I was writing down his. "Well, I worked in Des Moines and I lived in that house during the week. On the weekends, though, I would drive home to Lawrence. I was dating my wife back then. She was a senior in high school. So I would drive back to see her."

"You and your wife were high school sweethearts?"

"That's right." I heard him inhale, like he was pulling in a cigarette. When he spoke, I heard him blow smoke out before his words started. "I had a friend from Lawrence who got me a job in construction, and he was living in the house, so I moved in. My friend, he, uh . . . died a couple of years ago."

"Oh," I said. "I'm sorry."

"Yeah, he's dead, so . . . you can't talk to him. In fact, all the guys I lived with in that house are dead. You can't talk to any of them."

I blinked. I hadn't asked to talk to any of them. That was a strange thing to suddenly blurt out. "They're all dead?"

"Yup. All of them."

I kept quiet. I jotted it down.

Edward cleared his throat and changed the subject, "Do you drink alcoholic beverages?"

I let out a small laugh. "Me? Uh, yeah." I reached over and took a sip of the vodka lemonade that was sweating on my desk.

"You live in Johnston?"

"Right."

"Is there a place near you that serves alcoholic beverages where we could meet for lunch?"

I put my pen down. "Yes," I smiled. "I would be happy to have lunch with you." My mind started zipping through all the restaurants in the area. "I live about a mile away from Jethro's. Just off of 86th Street."

"Okay, let me write this down." I heard a page turn. "I would like to meet you for a beer. I want to see you with my own eyes. I think when I see you, I will know for sure. But my plan after that is to tell my wife about you. I would like to schedule a paternity test at a lab and, depending on the results, we will tell our boys."

"That sounds like a great plan," I said and started writing again.

Edward mumbled off the days of the week, talking to himself about his weekly schedule of lunch dates and golf games. "I can come over this upcoming Wednesday. That will work good for me."

I nodded. "I'm on spring break so Wednesday is good."

"You're not going to Hawaii or anything?"

I laughed. "No, not this year."

"Okay," he said. "I'll call on Tuesday with a time and to confirm with you."

"Sounds good."

He hesitated. "I really hate keeping this from my wife." He sighed. "I need you to know that I don't want you to get your hopes up or anything because I really don't think I'm your father."

SIXTEEN

There were two main things about my conversation with Edward that were red flags. The fact that he told me that all of the guys he lived with in that house were now dead and that he hadn't talked to any of his siblings for eight years.

I knew both were untrue. I understood the comments were made to keep me at an arm's distance. You can't be welcomed into a group of dead guys and if you're hoping to impress your new biological father, you sure don't want to ruin it by talking to his family, especially when he hasn't spoken to them for eight years.

All signs pointed to "No Entry."

But then there was the one thing about the conversation that overrode everything: he was willing to meet me. He wanted to see me, he wanted a paternity test, and he was going to tell his family. He had a plan.

Amy, the girls, and I all took this as very good news. We chattered about Edward all weekend. Amy called him adorable. The girls wanted to get their hair cut in case they would be able to meet him when he came to town on Wednesday.

"You never know," Catey said, hopeful. "He might like you so much that he won't be scared to meet us."

I didn't have the heart to argue with her

Right after our conversation, I plugged Edward's contact information into my phone so this time when he called, his name popped up. I answered on the first ring. "Hello?"

The first time I talked to Edward I would have described him as nervous, but this Edward was a notch above nervous. He was edgy, flustered, and scrambled.

"I can't meet you on Wednesday," he started with a bang. "I'd like to meet you tomorrow, if that's okay."

"Sure," I agreed. "I'm open all week."

"Okay, so tomorrow. Tomorrow is Tuesday, right?"

"Yes, it is."

Edward stumbled over a few words that I couldn't follow and then he became very clear: "I told my wife."

"Good," I said.

"Well, she's not taking it very well."

"Oh, I see." I felt the entire room tilt dangerously to the left and I had to sit down.

"I need to meet you tomorrow for a DNA test. I've been calling around Des Moines looking for a lab and I think I found one. You're flexible? You can meet up anytime tomorrow?"

"Yes," I nodded. "You pick the time and place and I will be there."

He thanked me and told me he would call back. I felt the excitement from the weekend fading away. Amy assured me this could be a positive thing. "He needed to tell his wife anyway," she pointed out.

He did, I knew that. But his plan was to meet me and then tell his wife. His plan was to wait six weeks and then contact me. He already wasn't very good at sticking with what he said he would do.

I had really just wanted that beer with him.

Edward called back several times that Monday, trying to nail things down. In the end, we agreed to meet on Tuesday at noon for a paternity test at LabCorp in Urbandale, a seven-minute drive for me, a three-hour-seven-minute drive for him.

"I should probably not drive the Buick," he was mumbling to me. "I don't want to get it dirty."

I ignored his ramblings. "How much does the test cost?" I asked. "I want to pay for half."

"Don't worry about it," Edward said. "I already paid the bill and, depending upon the results, we will settle it up if needed."

Got it. If I were his son, I would pay half; if I were a nephew, I would pay the entire amount. Personally, I thought both scenarios were fair.

After we hung up, I called LabCorp and asked how much a paternity test cost. "Five hundred fifty dollars," the receptionist said.

I told Amy and she immediately went to the bank and withdrew two-hundred-seventy-five dollars. "You are paying him half tomorrow," she said. "We are not going to be the kind of people who spring this kind of news on a person and then make him think that he is responsible for the entire bill."

I couldn't agree more. I stuffed the cash into my wallet.

The girls tiptoed around me that day. Catey asked if she could go with me to the appointment. I told her no, that it would be too much for Edward. Honestly, it would be too much for me, too. I spent the majority of the evening reminding myself that I had to keep my expectations low. That way I wouldn't be too disappointed.

Then I went to bed and lay awake all night long.

MARCH 14, 2017. TUESDAY.

The next morning, Amy was jittery. I noticed she had plucked her eyebrows and was wearing her good bra. "Just in case it goes well and I get to meet him," she said. "You got the money?"

I patted my ass, where my wallet was.

"Ask him to lunch. It's noon. Maybe he's hungry."

"Okay."

"Or at least a beer."

I grabbed my jacket. The sun was shining but it was a crisp thirty degrees outside. I drove the short distance to the lab. It was easy to find. On the drive, I tried not to think too much about what I was really doing. The reality of the situation started my heart pounding and my stomach would do flip flops so instead, I turned up the radio and sang all the way there. I pulled into the parking lot and pegged him right away. Out of the corner of my eye, I saw him get out of his truck. I met Edward Schneyder for the first time on the sidewalk in front of the LabCorp DNA lab. We walked easily toward each other.

"Michael?" He asked.

"Edward." No question needed.

Quickly, I noticed we were both wearing a ball cap, a flannel shirt, black leather jackets, blue jeans and we had on the same brand of tennis shoes.

"We didn't have to dress alike." I smiled and reached out to shake his hand.

Edward accepted my handshake, but he did not laugh at my joke. Tough crowd. Apparently a sense of humor skipped his generation.

"Let's do this," he said and he opened the door for me.

Once inside, Edward walked up to the reception area and gave his name. We didn't have to sit down, our names were called right away and we were taken back to a small exam room. A technician came in and explained the procedure. I tried to keep my attention on what she was doing and saying but my eyes kept drifting over to Edward, getting glimpses of his facial expressions, the way he folded his hands, watching him as he signed forms—he was right-handed, I was left. Huh, my mom was also right-handed. I always thought my biological father would be left, like me.

I was on high alert, absorbing every noise, comment, and tick he made. If he smiled, I smiled; if he cleared his throat, I cleared mine. I was trying to do whatever I needed to not upset this delicate balance.

A swab was stuck in my mouth and the technician tickled my cheek. She did the same to Edward and then she placed the swabs into their own sterile tubes and labeled them. It was done. Total time: seven minutes.

"Okay, you should get the results in three to ten days. But, on average, it takes about a week. Since you paid," the technician addressed Edward, "you will be sent the results via email."

Red flag.

"I don't get a copy?" I asked.

"No, the person who pays the fee gets the copy."

I didn't know that. I think both the technician and Edward could read the panic on my face because Edward spoke up. His voice was calming. "I will call you with the results and I will send you a copy."

"You will send me a copy of the email?" I asked to clarify because my brain was still stuck on the fact that I wasn't getting a copy and I needed him to repeat it so I knew I understood him correctly.

"Yes," he reassured me. "I have your email. It's on the letter you sent to me."

That's right. I remembered putting it there. I nodded. "Okay." I had to trust him on this. "I just . . . I need something tangible. Something to hold in my hands that says one way or another –"

"I know. I understand. I will send you a copy."

I opened my mouth to say something else but Edward beat me to it. "Can you give us a few minutes alone?" he asked the technician.

"Of course." She exited the room, closing the door behind her.

Edward turned to me. It was a surreal experience to finally look at him, to see his face, mine, all mine, plus twenty years of age. "Thanks for meeting me on such late notice."

"Sure," I said. We sat, looking each other up and down. I swallowed and took my chance. "Would you like to go grab a beer? I'm buying."

Edward took a breath. "I can't. I have to get back to Lawrence. My wife, Bev... she isn't doing very well with all of this." He gave a sad smile. I had seen that smile before in the mirror.

"She's not?"

"No. After I talked to you on Saturday, I told her. She took it really well that day and I thought things were going to be okay but then yesterday... she was different. And this morning, she was almost hysterical. She didn't want me to come here but I knew I had to." He paused. "We did get online and we looked at your Facebook. We were able to see everything on it and, uh, Bev thinks you resemble our oldest son."

I nodded. "You do?"

"*Bev* thinks that you do. Personally, I don't see a family resemblance."

I blinked and tried to keep the sarcasm off my widening grin.

"I saw the picture of you and your mother when you were young and..." he shook his head. "I don't remember her. I really don't think this test is going to come back positive. I don't think you're my son."

Sitting there, it was hard to tell if what he was saying was coming from a place of shock or guilt or if he was being sincere. "Well, if I'm not your son," I slowly explained, "then I'm your nephew. One of your brothers would be my father. Which one of them do you think it would be?"

Edward seemed like he was going to say a name but shook his head instead. No answer.

I pulled out my wallet and handed him the cash. "It's half," I said.

Edward waved a hand in refusal. "We will work it out after the results."

I tried again.

"I'm not taking it . . . today," he said as he stood up. His hand wandered over in my direction, so I grabbed it and shook it.

"You'll email me the results?" I asked again.

"Yeah," he said. "I'll call when they come in and send them right over to you."

Putting my trust into Edward was the first true test for both of us. I knew there was no way he could understand how important it was for me to have a solid piece of paper stating who my father was. That I was a complete person, made from this woman and this man. He had no idea about my birth certificate being sealed, had no knowledge of all the effort I had put into obtaining a document that was denied to me, and he had no idea of the secrets and lies that had been told to me my entire life. He didn't know how hard it was for me to put my trust in him.

"Okay." I agreed. I guess the best way to find out if I could trust Edward was to actually trust him.

Ten minutes later I was back at home in my kitchen. Amy glanced at the clock. "He didn't want to meet you for lunch?" She hadn't expected me home for at least another hour.

I shook my head. "No, he said he had to get back to Lawrence. His wife isn't handling this well."

She hugged me. The girls hugged me. I swallowed hard and tried to keep it together.

"Well," Amy asked, "what was your overall impression?"

I nodded and looked at her. "He's the guy."

SEVENTEEN

The Friday after meeting Edward was March 17. Amy's family participates in Des Moines' St. Patrick's Day Parade every year. Her dad has a fleet of parade vehicles, all decked out in green shamrocks and we march with his hometown of Melrose, Iowa. Leo, my father-in-law, dresses in a green suit, complete with green cowboy hat, green sneakers, and a shillelagh that he carries. In 2017, Leo was eighty-seven years young and walked the entire parade route. They call him Leo the Leprechaun. They call him Mayor. They call him the Godfather.

One hundred percent Irish.

I was thankful for the parade that year. I had not talked to Edward all week and had been checking my email obsessively. I needed the reprieve from the quiet of spring break to keep my mind busy. The parade was a great answer for that. After four hours spent with Amy's family, we met up with our neighbors at a local bar and partied with them.

"How are you doing with everything?" Kelly asked me.

I took in a deep breath. "I'm patiently impatient." That would become my mantra. Being patient was hard work because I wanted answers now. I was actively working on patience.

I thought of Edward and how he was doing in Lawrence. I could only assume that he was feeling similar anxiety but, in my case, while I was hoping for the results to come back definitive that he was my biological father, he was praying for the opposite.

St. Patrick's Day ended and we moved slowly through the weekend. Every day seemed to get longer than the day before. I could hardly wait for Monday to arrive—I had never wanted to go back to work so badly and our DNA results would surely be in.

I walked in the house at five o'clock on Monday and threw my jacket on the floor. "Goddammit!"

"They said it would be three to ten days," Amy reminded me.

She's just trying to be helpful, I told myself. "It's been a week! The technician said it would be a week!"

"On average. She said it would take three to ten days. You'll have the results this week."

"I want them NOW! I hate waiting!"

Tuesday came and at 5pm, I did a repeat performance of Monday. This time I stomped my feet in the kitchen and considered throwing my body on the floor and throwing a temper tantrum. Instead I drank four vodka lemonades and passed out early.

MARCH 22, 2017

On Wednesday, I finished my morning classes and was headed for lunch. Quickly I checked my phone and saw I had a missed call from Edward. I called him back. He answered right away.

"Yeah," he said, "I got the email and we're a match."

Everything inside of me lit up. It's difficult for me to even remember exactly what we said to each other because all of my senses were working overtime. It took all I had not to run through the halls of my building screaming, "I know who my father is! I know who my father is!" Instead, I swallowed a couple of times and calmly asked, "Okay, what exactly does that mean?"

Edward sounded terse. "We're a match. I'm your ... you're my...

it says we're father and son. It's something like ninety-nine percent positive."

"Okay, then."

Silence.

"We are having a hard time believing it," Edward quietly spoke.

We. I didn't say anything.

"We are going to need some time to let the results sink in and process this."

"Okay, I understand." I paused. "Thank you for calling. Would it be okay if I call you later and discuss it more? I have some questions for you. Medical stuff and things like that."

"Yeah," Edward said. "That would be fine."

I pocketed my phone and ran out to my car. I skipped food and drove straight home. Amy had been working nights so I knew she would be sleeping, but I also knew she would want me to wake her up so I ran up the stairs and burst into our bedroom. Amy sat straight up in bed, alarmed. Then she saw me. "What? What is it?"

"Ninety-nine percent!"

"Oh, my God!" She yelled. "Michael, you know who your father is!"

"I know!" I yelled back. I threw my arms out and spun around in a circle.

Amy and I stared at each other, feeling a surge between us, a combination of years of hard work and countless disappointment, to finally be here with the one answer we had sought so long for.

"Did he send you the email?" Amy asked.

"Not yet," I told her, breathless. "I need to text him and remind him to send it. I will do that when I get back to work." I still had my afternoon class to teach. I checked the clock. "I need to go and grab something to eat and get back." I walked over and kissed Amy on the forehead. "Sorry I woke you."

"I'm glad you did," she said. "I won't be able to get back to sleep now, but I'm glad you did."

I stopped for lunch and went back to work on a high. I stopped at my office, texted Edward about sending the email, and I went in and taught something—who the hell remembers what—to my students.

Two hours later I walked into my office and noticed a missed call from Edward. I locked my door and checked my email. Nothing. So I called Edward back. He answered right away.

"Hi, Michael," he sounded distant. "I did get that email from LabCorp and Bev and I looked at it. You and I are a match. It was ninety-nine percent or something. I'm online right now checking the validity of paternity tests. It might be an error."

It's not an error, I wanted to argue. Instead, I said, "Okay, that sounds fair. Could you go ahead and send over the email to me? I would like to have it."

"I deleted it."

I blinked.

"Bev and I looked at it and then we deleted it and removed it from our computer. Then I called LabCorp and told them that I needed them to delete it from their records and they said that they would do that."

I glanced up at the clock. It was 5:20pm. LabCorp would be closed by now. "You did?" I asked. "You had them deleted?"

"I did and I want you to know that they did exactly what I said. There is no evidence of us ever being there. I am leaving no trail of us behind. Bev and I are never telling anyone about you. Not our sons. Not my family. No one."

I closed my eyes. I could hear the clickety-clack of a rollercoaster pounding in my ears. Up, up, up, up, and then plummeting down at an unreal rate of speed. No bottom could be reached.

I was fucking pissed.

EIGHTEEN

Our first daughter, Rosie, entered the world thirteen days late, forcing me to wait, and changed my life again, gifting me my best title to date: Dad. Rosie was eight pounds, six ounces of beauty. She had my blue eyes, my off-centered nose, and her mother's chin. We counted all ten of her fingers and all ten of her toes. She was perfect.

The next day the doctor came in and told us Rosie had Coombs jaundice. She would be spending the rest of her hospital time under lights and having her bilirubin level monitored. When she went home, she would go home with bili lights. A visiting home nurse would come by daily to take blood draws.

"Is this kind of jaundice genetic?" I suddenly asked.

"It can be," the doctor said. "Do you have a history of it in your family?"

Amy shook her head. I shook mine. "Not on my mother's side but I don't know who my biological father is."

"Oh." The doctor shrugged. "I wouldn't worry too much. I have seen adoptees in here before with babies who have way worse things wrong with them than yours. She will be fine."

And she was. All went well, but what the doctor said was unnerving. All my adult life, I had explained to physicians that I didn't know my entire medical family history. It was never treated as a big deal.

Even when Amy was trying to get pregnant and suffered several miscarriages, she was the one who had to undergo the majority of the testing. Every time she went in to get a fallopian tube blown or have a biopsy of her uterine lining, I thought to myself—what if it's not her? What if it's me?

Then we landed Rosie and the pregnancy went off without a hitch. "The others were just flukes," we were told. " Don't worry. Now that you have had one successful pregnancy, more children are on your horizon."

Not knowing my entire medical history and having it affect me was one thing, now that we had Rosie and potentially more children to come, ignited a new fire inside me. I had other reasons to find my biological father other than just knowing his name. Now I wanted to know *who* he was.

It was 1999 when I started requesting my original birth certificate. Rosie had turned one and she looked so much like my baby photos. It was uncanny. Her mere existence made me wonder more about my own. Knowing Rosie for just one year made me curious about who else was out there. What other people had been missing in my life?

Two weeks after my request, I was denied and sent a copy of my delayed birth certificate. The letter contained information on placing a formal request with the courts to obtain my sealed birth certificate. So I did that and marched it down to the Lucas Building in downtown Des Moines. It was submitted and four weeks later, I received a denial from a judge and yet another copy of my delayed birth certificate.

I couldn't understand why I was getting the runaround when I was raised by my birth mother. Was my biological father's name on the original? Who were they protecting? It wasn't my mother. Was it me? Or was it him?

Before she met me, Amy had worked in medical records for

Methodist Hospital, where I had been born. She told me that sometimes she had to pull all the medical records on a person who had requested their entire records from the day they were born until present. She suggested that I try it. So I did.

It worked.

Even with my name being nothing more than Baby Boy Lang, the hospital sent all my medical records, including the day I was born. "I was six pounds, one ounce. I never knew that before."

"You were born at 1:29 in the morning," Amy pointed out." My birthday is January 29." She smiled. "One-twenty-nine."

"Weird," I agreed. The medical records were fairly thorough. My mother's nurse charted from the time my mom was admitted until she gave birth, the urgency of her notes heightening as delivery progressed. It was difficult to read. My mom struggled. "Mother screaming and not pushing." "Mother hyperventilating." "Sedative administered." "Nurse pushing on abdomen to get baby out."

And then, my birth. "Baby born at 1:29am. Cord wrapped around neck. Twice. Baby blue. Apgar 1. At five minutes, 5. At eight minutes, 8. Oxygen. Difficult birth due to mother's age and lack of experience."

I assumed that meant sexual experience. My mother turned eighteen in December, two months before I was born. I had a quick memory of being a teenager, sitting with my family, watching the Oprah Winfrey Show. There was a lady on, talking about her life, and she mentioned that she became pregnant the first time she had sex. "I had sex one time with my high school boyfriend and got pregnant!"

My sister Rachel laughed. "Seriously? Who gets pregnant on their first time?"

From across the room, my mom raised her hand.

"Really?" Rachel was shocked.

My mom shrugged. "Well, the second time." Then she laughed.

The last page of the medical records contained notes on my circumcision. Everything went well. Amy and I shared a thankful sigh of relief. "Whew!"

There was no mention of anyone being with my mom in the before, during, or after of labor. Not my grandmother, not my aunt, not a friend, certainly not a birth father. No one. The records made it sound like my mom gave birth to me alone.

Amy placed the records in the black folder and tucked them away in our safe. Another piece of paper about me, another piece of paper not leading to my biological father.

NINETEEN

I told Amy about my conversation with Edward and she assured me that no one at the lab had destroyed any of the DNA records. Even though I knew she was right, I couldn't help but panic that somehow, he convinced some young, new employee to get rid of all the evidence. Another night of sleep lost.

8:00am, the next day, I was on the phone with LabCorp. It took six different people, six different numbers, and six different states before I located the correct person. I explained to her my problem and that all I wanted was a copy of the email. I would pay another five hundred fifty dollars, if needed.

The lady acted like this happened all the time. "I have your results. What's your email . . . there. I sent it."

I had my laptop open already and my emails up. I hit the refresh button. Nothing. "Can you stay on the line for a few seconds until I receive it? I asked, a little bashful.

She chuckled. "Sure."

I hit refresh again. Nothing. "Can I give you my email again?" I hit refresh a third time. Boom. I had it. "Wait . . ." I clicked on it. "That's it," I said. I let out a held breath. "Thank you. Thank you so much."

I could hear her smile across the phone. "You're welcome."

I hung up and scrolled through the results and then hit print. I pulled the paper off my printer and walked upstairs to show Amy. She reached over and tried to take it but I couldn't let it go so she examined it over my shoulder.

There was a lot of scientific terms neither of us understood, but underneath all of it was the paragraph I had been waiting to read my whole life:

The alleged father, EDWARD SCHNEYDER, cannot be excluded as the biological father of the child, MICHAEL BLAIR, since they share genetic markers. Using the above systems, the probability of paternity is 99.99% as compared to an untested, unrelated man of the Caucasian population.

MARCH 26, 2017

Three days later, it was Sunday. I was downstairs, working and listening to the radio. *Alive* by Pearl Jam came on and just as if it were second nature, my head started bouncing to the music. The first few verses from Eddie Vedder, singing to his own mother, who hid the identity of his biological father as well. I turned up the volume and sang the words at the top of my lungs.

I couldn't help but think of Edward and considered maybe I should write him another letter when my phone rang.

It was Edward.

"Hello?" I answered. There was no small talk, no friendly exchange. I asked how things were going there and he replied, "Not good. We are having a hard time accepting this ... that these results are true."

I held my breath. "I'm sure it's been shocking news for you and Bev."

"She's not taking it well. Not at all," he said. "She broke out in hives. She's had a hard time breathing. Last night she complained she was having chest pain. In fact, she's at the doctor's office right now."

"Oh, she is?" That was not the kind of reaction I wanted anyone to have in hearing the news that I existed. I felt immediate guilt that my presence had caused her pain.

"She's pissed off at me and you and... she's just pissed. She's worried that people are talking about her. She is a very private person and she's convinced that the entire town is talking about this." There was a pause and then he asked, "Have you talked to anyone about the results?"

"Just my family," I replied.

"You haven't talked to Louisa?"

"No."

"Have you reached out to Carolyn?"

"You asked me not to," I said. Edward didn't say anything, so I added, "No, I haven't."

He hesitated. "Have you told your mother?"

"Not yet."

Edward sighed. "Well, I would appreciate it if you didn't tell her."

I frowned. "Why? What do you think she's going to do?"

"I don't know," Edward said. "But I don't need another person to worry about. I don't want her to know so I would appreciate it if you wouldn't tell her." He was curt. And then he added, "But I guess you're going to do whatever you're going to do. I mean, who am I?"

Yeah, who are you? I wanted to reiterate but instead I responded, "I am not planning on telling her right now."

"Okay, good." He quieted. I could feel the frustration on the other line. "I don't remember her . . . your mother, that is."

"You don't?"

"No. What did she tell you about meeting me?"

I waivered. So far, I had not been impressed with the way that Edward had handled things. I decided to keep my mother's story close to my vest for now. "She hasn't told me a whole lot."

"Okay," he seemed more at ease. "Let me tell you what I remember because I'm going to be honest—I have no idea how you got here or how you are *mine*. Shortly after high school, I took off and went to Oregon for a while...it's a long story...but I was working with a buddy of mine. I stayed there for a few months before coming back to Iowa. I had a friend who was living in Des Moines. He and some other guys from Lawrence were renting a house and were working construction. They offered me a job, so I took it. One night, we were all hanging out when one of the guys came home with a woman. One of the other guys had been dating this woman's friend. Anyway, the woman got into a big fight with her boyfriend and he kicked her out of his house and she didn't have anywhere to go so she stayed the night with us. I only met her briefly and then she and the other guy went into his bedroom. He shut the door and they were in there all night doing...you know, doing whatever they were doing."

Sex. He was implying she was having sex with the guy.

"Anyway, I went to sleep and when I woke in the morning, I had a naked woman on top of me. She started kissing me and bouncing up and down and...we didn't have sex. I mean, it was close, I guess, but I had my underwear on the entire time. There was absolutely no penetration and I don't know how you are here."

This? This was his story? "Well," I replied, "I have always been a very strong swimmer."

Edward didn't laugh. "As far as I know...I mean, I'm pretty sure that your mother spent the night with more than just one of my friends that night."

Whore. Now he was calling my mom a whore. I felt my body heat up with anger. I took two deep breaths before responding. "Well, my mom wasn't a woman. She was seventeen. She was a junior in high school."

Silence. And then, "She was?"

"Yeah, and she didn't live with a boyfriend. In fact, she didn't even have a boyfriend back then. She lived at home with my grandparents."

More silence. "Well, I may have gotten some of the details wrong. It was a long time ago. She might have been kicked out by her father."

Edward sure seemed to have the details on point just a minute ago.

"I only remember all this because I was embarrassed because I had my underwear on and I . . ." he trailed off. "Ejaculated in them."

This was the dumbest story I had ever been told. How fucking dimwitted did this guy think I was?

"My mom was seventeen," I repeated. "She was a junior when she got pregnant and when she went back to school for her senior year, the administration forced her to drop out. My grandpa was pretty tough on her and he made sure she got a job. She couldn't go to college because of me. She had to work two and three jobs until she met my dad and was able to finally move out. She had a hard time for quite a few years."

Edward was quiet. "I didn't need to know all of that."

Yes, you did. But, I bit my tongue. "That was only part of it," I said.

Before I could go further, Edward slowed his words down and said, "I don't feel a bond with you. I don't feel a bond, I have no regrets, and I don't feel a connection with you."

I had been keeping my expectations low but even that was tough to hear. "I get that," I said. "But if you just found out about me, those things might take some time."

"Listen," Edward began and then he hesitated. I wasn't sure where he was going to go next, then he blurted out, "I'm the victim here."

"You are?" I challenged, and because I couldn't believe he just said that, I repeated, "You are?"

"Yes, I am the victim in this situation." He was growing more agitated. "I can't . . . we are having a hard time believing this test is true. And I . . . look, Bev is going to be home soon. I have to go."

I nodded. "Okay, well, do you want to give this a week and let things settle in?" I suggested. "Maybe we can talk next Sunday and see how things are going?"

Silence.

"Or we can let it go now? We don't have to talk again. You can . . ." I almost said "walk away" but that came with a lot of truth and weight. Instead I went with, "I would like to get some questions together about your family's medical history."

Edward let out a breath. "I'll talk to you next Sunday," he said. "I'll call you before noon. Don't call me."

TWENTY

There were a few things about Edward's story that rubbed me the wrong way:

1. Jizzing in your underwear does not make a baby.
2. For a dry hump, he sure did remember a lot about it.
3. If my sister called me and told me that I had a long-lost son and I knew the only sexual misstep I ever had was ruining a pair of underwear years before, I would have never thought the baby was mine. I would have told her to call one of my other brothers. No way in hell that I was the father because....
4. Jizzing in your underwear does not make a baby.

It wasn't that I didn't believe Edward's story. I did. I just felt that this encounter he was recalling was not with my mother. Either he truly did not remember my mom, or he was choosing not to remember her. Either way, I had to laugh at the way he portrayed her—there was this woman, kicked out of the house by her boyfriend, having sex with every guy in the house—not Edward, of course—just the four other guys. Edward was the innocent. How the hell my mother had sex with up to four men but only hopped up and down on Edward's underwear, somehow getting pregnant with his baby was beyond me.

I remembered a scene from the movie *Meatballs* when newly arriving campers were moving in and over at the girls cabin, some young fourteen year old girls were having a debate about the different ways you could become pregnant. One girl cautioned her friends, saying she heard of a girl who got pregnant when she had on her underwear. Surprised, the campers asked their counselor, a much older eighteen-year-old female, who broke out into a big grin and answered them, "No! You can't get pregnant if you're wearing underwear!" Then they all broke out into laughter.

Pregnancy with your underwear on wasn't even a possibility in a Bill Murray comedy.

Amy and I were moving forward as best we could, trying to hold on to the positive. We were having friends over for a surprise "Who's Your Daddy" party. My friends, people who had been a part of my journey from day one, were enamored by the story. Amy and I took turns telling it, each one talking over the other at different peaks and valleys. She was better at telling the facts and timetables; I was better at filling in the conversations and emotions.

Everyone wanted to know about siblings. Did I have any? Had I told them? We gave them a rundown on the three men—my half-brothers—and each one of my friends had the same reaction: Forget the oldest and concentrate on the other two.

"No," I replied. "His past doesn't matter to me. I want to get to know him just as much as I want to get to know the others." And that was the truth. The fact that Edward and Bev's oldest son had run-ins with the law did not deter me. He was my brother and if he were ever interested in knowing me, I was in.

"When are you going to tell them?" Our friends asked.

I shrugged. "I'm hoping Edward and his wife will do that." I didn't want to tell three grown strangers that they had a long-lost brother. I really hoped their father would break the news to them. I thought it was important for Edward to have that conversation with his sons so he could present his own version of the story.

I wasn't sure what I would do if he never got there.

What I didn't want was for any of them to find out secondhand, which was becoming more of a real possibility. One thing we did not bank on when we told our friends and family about finding Edward was how many people would comment, "Oh, I have friends in Lawrence" or "My son-in-law is from Lawrence" or "I know some Schneyders" or "I know your brother Mark."

There were some close connections.

Plus, there was Ancestry.com. I was out there now, like a beacon, waiting for someone to spit in a tube "just for fun" and send in their sample. I was just a Mother's or Father's Day gift away from hitting another family relationship. I had already received two messages from second cousins whom I had not replied to, out of respect to Edward.

This train wasn't going to stop anytime soon. From mouth-to-mouth gossip to actual DNA evidence, the cat was indeed out of the bag. It was all just a matter of time.

My friends were texting on a regular basis. "How are things going?" "Have you talked to him again?" "I told my parents and their cousin lives in Lawrence—they are going to ask if they know Edward!" "Have you told your mom yet?"

It was all making me sick. I had to do something. I decided to break my pact with Edward and place a phone call to Louisa. She had been my point of original contact, she had been the one Edward had named to act as a liaison. I needed to talk to someone, and I felt like if it were going to be anyone, I could make an exception for Louisa.

I texted her and we made a plan to phone that evening. Unlike speaking with Edward, talking with Louisa seemed to come like the snap of a finger. She was warm and intelligent and shed light on life in Lawrence. It seemed the Schneyder name had been there for a few generations now. Her parents, of course, had lived there and farmed land. There were many extended aunts, uncles and cousins. The name Schneyder wasn't uncommon in their part of Iowa. There were not many, but they had a swell of pride in their name and where they came from.

Louisa was surprised to hear that I had already spoken to Edward and that he had made the trip to Des Moines to take the paternity test. She was shocked to hear we already had the results and that he and Bev were holed up in their house, processing the news. Edward hadn't mentioned a word to her about any of it. The family, according to her, was fractured. Ever since their parents died, the ten kids had split, each forming alliances with other siblings. "This one is mad at that one or that one isn't speaking to this one. Honestly, it changes so often, I have trouble keeping it straight sometimes."

She started throwing out names and I couldn't follow. There were just too many of them and they muddled my mind.

"That's what it's like living in Lawrence, though," she said. "Everyone is in each other's business, whether you want them to be or not. I mean, I have talked openly with my husband and my son about you and even a few close friends and all of them agree that this doesn't have to be the big deal that Edward and Bev seem to be making it out to be." She paused. "But I haven't lived in Lawrence since the early seventies. It sounds like Edward's main focus has been on who knows. I think he has gone into protective mode, for Bev's sake. They have a lot on their plate already and he's just trying to protect his family. Ed really is a good guy."

That made me feel better. Louisa was right—that's all this was—just a guy trying to protect his family from small-town gossip. He had said that Bev was a very private person. Louisa mentioned that Bev had lost her father when she was young and grew up an only child. Even though she had been in the Schneyder family for more than forty years, it had been an adjustment going from being an only child to being married to one of ten.

I nodded. Okay. Louisa said Edward was a good guy. Of course he was. He was a good man because even though he was being an asshole and trying to make my mom sound like she was a whore in high school and that her getting pregnant had nothing to do with him, he had good inside of him.

"He hasn't mentioned anything about me, though?" I asked, a little disappointed.

"No," she said. "I haven't heard from him since he sent me the email. Then I, of course, sent you the message about being a contact person for both of you. Until I heard from you, I thought we were still waiting the six weeks. I had no idea."

Again, this surprised me. If I was going through something big in my life, like an unexpected child, I would talk to my sisters about it. I would talk to Amy's family about it. I wouldn't shut down.

Dirty Little Secret. It whispered to me in the back of my mind. First my mother, now Edward. I was never going to shake it.

"Hopefully Ed will talk with me or someone about it because it will be good for him to speak about things. Get it off his chest. I did call him about something else last week and when he answered the phone, I could tell he was apprehensive that I was going to ask about you ... but then I didn't, and I sensed his relief. He seemed okay with our conversation. I won't be the one to ask about you, though. I will let him come to me."

I frowned. "Why? Are you afraid of him?"

"Not afraid," Louisa said. "It's more about ..." She thought about it, "Respect."

"Okay," I said but I didn't believe her. This wasn't respect. Respect for what? Respect was when you showed admiration for someone's actions. This wasn't guided by respect. This was guided by fear.

"Patience," Louisa said. "Ed is a very thoughtful person. He's going to need time to think this through."

Hanging up the phone, I put my trust in Louisa's words. I had to. I needed to believe her because I needed to know that I came from good.

I sighed and went upstairs. Amy smiled. "Do you feel any better about things?"

I sighed. "You have a dysfunctional family. I have a dysfunctional family." I shook my head. "Why the hell do we want another dysfunctional family?"

TWENTY-ONE

My next conversation with Edward was a complete one-eighty from the last one. He was engaging, open, and funny. He laughed at my jokes and was easy to talk to.

"Where are you?" I asked him. It sounded like he was moving.

"I'm driving around Lawrence, smokin' cigarettes."

He shared with me how his parents died. Amy and I had made a list of medical questions in our notebook and I wrote his answers down. Cancer. "What kind?" Lung. "Did his father smoke?" Of course. They all seemed to smoke.

Alzheimer's. Alcoholism. Breast cancer...pretty much everything that was in any random person's family medical history.

Edward talked a bit about the aftermath of being the executor of his parents' wills and how it caused some rifts in the family. He talked about his own health and the heart attack he suffered a few years before. "I have probably had a dozen heart attacks," he said.

"A dozen?" I was shocked.

"When I had the big one, I realized what a heart attack felt like and I realized I had probably had a few already."

The "big one" he referred to was the Widow Maker. Amy explained to me that it was a large blockage in the main left artery and that it is a critical location. Without surgery, it is almost always suddenly fatal, hence being referred to as the Widow Maker.

Edward changed topics and talked easily about that first year after high school, traveling to Portland, Oregon, and about his time spent in Des Moines. "I learned a lot about construction. When I moved back to Lawrence, my job took me all over the state. I did road construction and then eventually started building houses and buildings. That's what I did. I owned my own business, Gateway Construction. I sold it years ago and retired when I was forty-eight."

"Wow," I said. "Forty-eight. That's amazing."

He talked about Bev. She wasn't doing any better with the news. She was nervous to the point that she was sometimes hysterical. "She wants to sue Ancestry," he told me. "She doesn't understand how they can just match people's DNA up and not have repercussions. Where are the ethics in that? Where are the privacy laws?"

"I see," I said. Bev wanted to keep me a secret. It was the classic question from the movie *The Matrix*—do you take the blue pill or the red? Choose the blue pill and life stays as it is, although an illusion. Choose the red pill and the veil will be pulled back, you will live in the truth, even if it proves to be undesirable. Once you choose the red pill, your choice has been made and there's no going back.

Personally, I would choose the red pill again and again, but what if someone takes the red pill for you? You're forced to see the truth, even though you would have preferred living in the illusion of the blue pill.

"Every time she sees an AncestryDNA commercial, she cries and screams. Yesterday she threw the remote at the TV."

I started to say something but all that came out was, "Oh."

"She told me that if you had shown up ten or twenty years ago, she would have left me."

I wondered how true that was. What was different about this timing? Did she feel they were too old to divorce? She didn't feel secure enough in leaving? What was different now that wasn't the same twenty years ago?

Grandchildren, I thought. Bev could handle the thought of some people finding out about me but she couldn't disappoint their grandkids. Explaining that grandpa had another child out there that he never knew—and that man wasn't grandma's child—was a lot to explain to young minds. Too many questions.

"I want to tell my friend Max about you," Edward suddenly said. "I tell Max everything. I feel like I need to bounce things off someone and just . . . tell someone."

I shrugged. "Then tell Max."

"I can't. She won't let me. I've already asked."

I felt bad for him. I was able to tell anyone I wanted. I talked about it openly on a daily basis and here Edward was, carrying this burden in silence. For me, everything was able to be transparent; for Edward, everything was still cloaked in scandal. I felt like Bev asking him to keep quiet was only feeding Edward's shame.

"Bev told me that I can only talk to two people about all of this. Her and you. And, believe me, the two of you have completely different outlooks on the situation."

I ended our phone call the same way as the last: "Do you want this to be our last conversation or do you want to talk next Sunday?"

Edward was laughing about something when he answered me. I can't for the life of me remember why, but I remember his laugh as he replied, "Sure, next Sunday is fine. You call me this time."

TWENTY-TWO

I spent the first five years after Rosie arrived easing into father-hood. And by easing, I mean if she threw up on me, I threw up. If I walked into a room and could smell her diaper, I would offer Amy $1,000 if she would change her. If Rosie stuck her lip out and pouted, I caved and gave her what she wanted. If she needed me to put on a tutu and wig, I gladly did it, with a Barbie in my left hand and a beer in my right.

I loved being a father and I felt like I had it down. I was good at it. I was a natural.

Then Amy announced she was pregnant again.

APRIL 2003

From the moment the stick turned blue, Amy's second pregnancy was much different from the first. She was sick every day, her mom died halfway through, and she developed preeclampsia, a pregnancy disorder that causes your blood pressure to rise to dangerous levels. The cure for it is birth.

Amy was induced one week early. Catey's birth was scary. We were in a normal birthing room, but Amy's bed was draped in seizure pads because of the preeclampsia and alarms were going off every-where. As Catey was getting close to making her appearance, I heard a nurse read Amy's blood pressure as 262/151. The doctor kicked the chair out behind her, just like they do in the movies, and she shouted, "We have to get this baby out!" She clapped her hands at Amy and yelled, "Push! NOW!"

And, somehow, Amy did exactly what she was supposed to do. In less than a minute we had a brand-new screaming human to get to know.

Amy laughed at her first sight of Catey. "Michael, she looks just like my mom! Look at her profile! Look at her face! I gave birth to my mom!"

Yup, she was right. This new kid definitely resembled Amy's side of the family.

Eight months later, Amy came home from the doctor and started crying. "I'm pregnant again."

I looked up from a mound of stuffed animals and Littlest Pet Shop toys. "What? I thought you couldn't get pregnant without fertility treatments." I pointed to the girls. "That's how we got those two."

Amy shrugged. "It looks like I got pregnant the same way all my friends did: I got drunk and had unprotected sex."

The preeclampsia came fast this time. According to the doctors, Amy's body had not completely recovered from Catey's birth. This time, she was on bed rest at twenty-eight weeks and was hospitalized at thirty-two weeks to keep the baby in as long as possible. In September 2004, five weeks before she was due, Jillian was born. She was what the nurses called a "near-term preemie." Jillian looked like me. Same eyes, same nose. Like Rosie, she had jaundice and we went home with bili-lights.

My father-in-law, Leo, came over every Sunday to do a donut drop, bring his used Sunday newspaper, and to spend ten minutes loving on the girls. He grabbed Jillian out of my arms and stared at her. "She's yours," he said, shaking his head. Leo, who had lived through six kids of his own, sensed my growing doubt that I could do this. "These girls are going to beat the shit out of you, Michael," he said. "You just roll with their punches. Don't ever give up and, remember, it's okay to let them hit you sometimes."

That was Leo-talk for keep calm, keep moving, and remember to always be open to grow and evolve.

"One day you'll look back and realize these are the happiest days of your life," Leo said.

He told me this as I had one kid wrapped around my leg, bawling her eyes out, another one calling me a "poopy head" and the third had just thrown up all over my favorite Dave Matthew's Band t-shirt. I smiled at Leo. Old people were always saying crazy shit like that.

The months following Jillian's birth dragged on for me and while it should have been one of the happiest times in my life, I found myself depressed. That old nagging voice in the back of my head had returned. I wanted to find my biological father.

Amy pulled out the black folder and I paged through it, every piece of paper not worth a damn in helping me.

"We've exhausted what we can do," Amy told me. "Maybe you want to talk to some kind of professional."

I had no idea who would handle something like this. I had a friend who knew a private investigator, so I contacted him and enlisted his help. He and I met a couple of times. What resulted in that waste of money was he couldn't find any nameless man and he thought my birth certificate was fraudulent. The private investigator's research found that a Delayed Certificate of Birth was issued in the early to mid-1900's when mothers would have their babies at home in the middle of winter and the fathers commonly would drive into the big city at the first sign of spring and would register the baby with the county clerk. They were then issued a Delayed Certificate of Birth. The investigator thought my parents may have just added me to their taxes and eventually a birth certificate was generated for me. He couldn't find any adoption paperwork and told me he didn't think my dad had ever legally adopted me.

I took his paperwork and filed it in the black folder.

Next, I consulted a lawyer. I explained my dilemma. She told me to petition the courts. I explained I had already done that, and her advice then was to wait. "Laws change. Maybe you'll catch a break in your lifetime and original birth certificates in Iowa will be unsealed."

In my lifetime?

I reserved time every Saturday for the next two months to go to the public library and scan through their years of microfiche, searching the mid-1970's newspapers for the advertisement that my parents supposedly had placed before my dad adopted me. I found nothing.

After talking to a friend who was a birth mother and had given up an infant, she told me she had recently reunited with her daughter via an adoptees website. I researched several websites all across the nation and registered with every one of them. *It doesn't hurt anything,* I thought. I checked it weekly for messages. Then monthly. Then yearly . . . and then about every three years, or whenever something jarred my memory that my name was on these registries. I never received any kind of a response.

I was feeling overwhelmed. Every day I woke up, I felt like my neck was caught in a vice. Every day I went to work, I couldn't concentrate. Every night I came home, I lay awake for hours, wondering. I ended up taking a couple of weeks off from work. I went to a therapist.

"You carry the pain of the question mark," she told me. "You don't know who you are."

"I don't think anyone ever knows who they really are," I replied.

"True, but you don't know where you originated from. Not entirely. You don't know where your roots are sunk in. Now that you have a family, you are connected to them, an invisible line reaches from you to your girls. But the line that reaches behind leads you to your mother and it ends in a question mark. That causes you pain."

She was right. "I'm never going to find who my biological father is," I said. "It's the one thing I have ever wanted and I'm never going to know."

"You're going to have to stop fighting it," she said. "You have to learn to embrace the question mark."

TWENTY-THREE

APRIL 2017

My life on Sundays hadn't changed much. I slept in an hour longer, woke up, took my shower, had coffee with Amy, and checked in with the three girls to see what the plan was that afternoon.

Things were different from 10:00am to 11:00am. This was the timeframe when Edward called. Sundays became something I looked forwarded to and equally dreaded. The actual phone calls with him either went smooth or they were volatile.

I noticed if Edward called from his car, cruising the streets of Lawrence, smoking cigarettes, the conversation was comfortable and uncomplicated. However, if he was at home when we spoke, the conversation was tense and distressed. It made me wonder if Bev was sitting next to him.

Conversations in his car contained information he gave out—without realizing he was doing it. He talked about growing up in Lawrence, how he graduated in the top ten percent of his class—"There are some big brains in this family." He discussed his parents, told me about odd jobs he did around the town for free, shared his love of golf, and recalled vacations he had taken. He rarely mentioned their boys, but he talked a lot of Bev and what he should do about her continuing difficult reaction.

"She's sick all the time. She can barely get out of bed. This is killing her," he would say one moment. Then the next he would tell me, "We went to Branson with some friends last week. You ever been?"

He put a great deal of emphasis on Bev's elderly mother who still lived on her own at home. "She's getting weaker. She fell a couple of months ago and we are going to have to place her soon." He paused. "If she ever found out about you, it would bury her. She would die of a heart attack right then and there." Sometimes he made it sound like if Bev's mom was out of the picture, then we would have a better shot at a relationship. "Bev still wants to please her mother. She doesn't like it when she upsets her. Bev worries every day about her mother finding out about you."

If Edward called from home, the conversation started off poorly and only went down from there.

"What's your end game with all of this?" he asked in April. "What are you hoping to accomplish?" He had been agitated with me since I answered the phone.

I took a breath. My end game? Honestly, I thought it had been to just know the name of my bio-father. Then I thought it was to meet him. Now, I realized my end game was much larger than I originally thought: I wanted to meet my half-brothers. I didn't want to disclose that to Edward, though. I kept my answer in the moment, what did I want my next step to be?

"I'd like to meet with you again," I replied. Our meeting at the lab, while I appreciated it, wasn't exactly ideal.

"Why?" He was terse.

Why? Was he serious? "Because I would like to sit across the table from you. I want to have lunch and share a beer with my biological father. I am half of you." I knew that saying it out loud would be tough for him to deny.

Edward didn't say anything.

"I'd like to talk in person for a while," I tried.

There was a long pause. "Oh, okay."

"So would you like to meet again?"

He was hesitant. "Give me some time to think about it and I'll get back to you."

I hung up the phone. I wanted Edward to *want* to meet me. I didn't want him to feel like he was being forced. One thing that I had desired from the beginning was to have things happen as organically as possible. I didn't want Edward to feel like I was strongholding him to these phone calls and, yet, the longer we talked and the more that I learned about him and his family, I found that I wanted more. Louisa and I shared a couple of email exchanges and I noticed that halfway through her notes, I would find myself smiling. Through her and Edward, they started painting a picture of my aunts, uncles, and cousins. They were becoming more real to me and I was feeling connections to some of them, even if they didn't know I existed yet.

I also started wondering about my half-brothers. How could I not? I looked at their Facebook pages and would marvel at our physical likeness to one another. I grew up with two sisters and although I could see similarities to both of them, their features were feminine and any resemblance to me was lost in makeup and hair.

But, my half-brothers—these were guys. Through all their ruggedness and masculinity I could see it easily—I looked like them.

"The more I look at you, the more I see our oldest son in you. I see some of our youngest, too," Edward commented. Hearing this, knowing I was remaining hidden, hurt. There wasn't anything I could do about that.

However, it was time for me to tell someone in my family.

As it happened, my niece Emily was going to Prom and I had agreed to meet up with my youngest sister, Rachel, and a group of parents to take pictures of everyone. I texted Rachel before I left and asked her if she were up to grab a drink after the photoshoot. *"I have something I want to talk to you about,"* I texted.

She texted back, *"Sure, I have an hour to kill afterwards."*

I showed up to take the pictures at 4pm and by 6:00, I was buying a couple of beers for me and Rachel at the High Life Lounge. Rachel is tiny, blond, blue-eyed, and has a quiet nature about her that attracts attention. She settled in across from me and said, "This is about your dad, isn't it?"

Rachel took me by surprise. "How did you know?" I ignored the word *dad*, I hadn't assigned any kind of name besides Edward to Edward.

"I just had a feeling," she said. "What have you found out?"

I met her eyes and grinned. "I found him."

"What?" Pure surprise.

"I found him. I know who he is."

"Shut up! How?" She took a big drink. "Who is he? What's his name? Does he live around here? Did he know about you? Do you have any siblings?"

I put my hand up, silencing her and then I filled her in on Ancestry.com and the at-home DNA kit. "His name is Edward Schneyder." I showed her a picture I had taken from Facebook.

"Wow," Rachel held my phone. "What's his name again?"

"Edward Schneyder," I repeated as I showed her photos of my half-brothers.

"Wow." Rachel shook her head. "I can't believe this."

I told her how Edward and I had been conversing the past few Sundays and how it was hot and cold. I filled her in on Edward's story about how he met our mother and how I was conceived.

Rachel listened. When I was done, she said, "That doesn't sound like Mom. I can't see her doing that."

"Me, either."

"I mean, it's possible that happened. Except, he's lying about the sex."

"Right."

"They had to have sex. People don't get pregnant with their underwear on."

"I know." Of course, it was possible. It had been documented as happening before but the chances that me being conceived by an underwear-clad man were extremely rare. I had Googled it and it was so rare that there wasn't even a percentage available of women whom this had happened to. Everything written about it would use terms as "extremely low chance," "almost impossible" and a few articles suggesting that the couple were lying about the fact that they had sex or that they simply didn't remember it happening.

"That's going to be a problem for you," Rachel said. "If he can't admit today that he had sex with a girl forty-six years ago, this probably isn't going to end well."

I nodded. Rachel was probably right. But, if there was a chance she was wrong, I had to stay in the game.

"Have you told Mom?"

I shook my head. "No."

"When are you planning on doing that?"

"I don't know. Soon." We finished our beers.

"How are you doing with all of this? How are you feeling?"

I grimaced. "I feel like I'm on a roller coaster all the time. One minute things are going well and I feel like I can do this and this isn't the biggest mistake of my life. Then the next minute, things aren't going well and I'm sick to my stomach and I feel like I'm ripping a marriage apart. I feel guilty, like I'm walking on eggshells and I think every minute of the day—this is going to be the moment that I throw up everywhere."

Rachel smiled. "Well, I was going to tell you that I'm really happy for you and I think it's wonderful."

I blinked. "Wonderful? I hadn't thought of it that way. Wonderful."

TWENTY-FOUR

After our last conversation, Edward asked for "some time" to think about meeting so I had decided I wouldn't reach out to him for a couple of weeks. As it would happen, the Sunday following our conversation was Easter. We hadn't discussed what to do if one of the Sundays landed on a holiday. I doubted Edward would make contact with me.

That Sunday we were extra busy. Not only was it Easter, it was also Catey's fourteenth birthday. She had a sleepover the night before and our house was full of parents picking up their daughters, dressed in pajamas and dragging around pillows and sleeping bags. Amy was a swarm of energy because that afternoon we were hosting Easter/Catey's Birthday Party with my family.

Shortly after 10am, just as the traffic in our house hit a peak, my phone rang. I glanced down and saw it was Edward calling. I shot Amy a look over the heads of noisy, unsuspecting parents, and Amy nodded in acknowledgement. I opened the basement door and took the call in my office.

It was short.

"Michael, this is Ed."

"Hi, Edward, how are you? Happy Easter," I said.

"Listen, I'm not going to meet you. This is as far as this thing is going to go."

I felt my stomach drop. "Okay," I said.

"I don't remember your mother. She came into that house that night and she wasn't just with me. You need to get it through your head that you were not intended."

"Believe me, I understand that."

"This situation is hard to control. I don't know who knows about you and who is talking about us. We feel like everyone we see in town already knows. Bev is a *mess!* She is not on board with this!" He paused. "I cannot meet you!"

Situation. Control. They were words I had to push out of my head. Edward was in trouble with his wife. That's what this was about. "I haven't talked to anyone except for my own friends and family," I told him. Which was a lie. I had talked to Louisa and emailed her twice but I felt that she was a vault and I could trust her—I felt Edward could trust her. She wasn't going to blab to anyone about our *situation.*

"I might feel different about you if I had a relationship with your mother or if it was more than what it was." He was quiet. "I don't have ownership over you. I did nothing that I regret. I don't feel any obligation to you."

I nodded. "Okay, well, what comes next?"

"I don't want to meet you."

"What do you want to do?"

Silence. He didn't know. Or, if he did know, he wasn't ready to say it.

"How about," I cleared my throat. "How about we don't talk for two weeks and I will call two Sundays from today and we can see if things have calmed down. Maybe we can think about what we both want, and we can decide at that time what happens next."

"Okay," Edward quickly agreed.

"Okay," I said. He wasn't ready to let me go. Not yet. Regardless of his words, there was something between us. He felt it, just as I did. He wasn't ready to give up on whatever that was. "Two weeks," I said.

"Two weeks," he repeated and we hung up.

I gathered myself a little before I headed upstairs. During our conversation, I could hear the faint pitter-patter of feet above me, muffled voices, and closing doors. It had been quiet for about five minutes and I figured all of the party-goers had ventured home. I walked up the stairs and found Amy and all three of the girls gathered in the kitchen, picking up the mess left from the night before, while simultaneously preparing for the next party.

"Everyone gone?" I asked.

"Last one just left," Amy nodded.

I smiled and kept my voice even. "That was Edward."

The girls were in earshot and stopped what they were doing. Catey suddenly perked up. "Edward called? Did he remember my birthday?"

I shook my head. "No, honey. Edward has no idea that today is your birthday."

She frowned. "Why did he call? Because of Easter?"

"No," I replied. "He called because he told me he doesn't want to meet me." I couldn't look at anyone. My heart was beating but I didn't feel alive. I felt empty, which, ironically, felt surprisingly heavy.

"He really doesn't know that today is my birthday?" Catey asked again.

I shook my head. "No, Catey. He doesn't know that it's your birthday. He doesn't know when any of your birthdays are. Honestly, he doesn't care about any of you."

Catey looked at me. Her face melted into abrupt sadness and she burst into tears.

TWENTY-FIVE

Easter Sunday ended as crappy as it started. After we hosted my family for dinner and had an Easter egg hunt, Amy and I wandered outside to talk with our neighbors. We live in one of those neighborhoods where the majority of us are friends. We know the names of many neighbors, their kids, and their pets. We have football scrimmages in our backyards, dog-sit puppies, and we know all the garage codes, in case we need to break into someone's house for a cup of sugar. It's the best.

We were hanging out with them when I heard a ding on my iPhone. I looked up at Amy. "I just received a friend request from Edward and Bev Schneyder."

Amy glanced at it. "It's a mistake," she said. "Bev was probably on your Facebook, looking around to see if you posted anything today and she must have hit friend request by accident." Amy shook her head. "It's a mistake."

"But what if it isn't?" I pressed confirm and immediately Edward and Bev's joint Facebook page was available to me. I scrolled through their Easter pictures, their middle son in attendance, with his family. I read a couple of posts about a past memory of a concert Bev had attended in Des Moines. I was able to see everything—for seven minutes—and then my phone froze. I backed out and when I tried to access the page again, I had been defriended. "Son of a bitch!" I yelled.

I don't know why I was so upset. I knew Amy was right, just like I knew my sister Rachel was right. Of course it was an error. Bev's finger slipped when it shouldn't have. That's all. But there was something that I had been hanging onto that I hadn't planned on: hope. All this time, I told myself to keep my expectations low and to not hold out any hope that this man would accept me into his family. But here I was, pissed off that a friend request on Facebook had been rescinded. Rejected again.

A few days later my middle sister Gina forgot something at our house from Easter. I told her to just bring her family over for dinner. So, she, her husband Matt, and their two sons came over. Before we sat down to eat, I took a breath, "I have some news."

Gina froze, she looked me up and down and then Amy. "Is everything okay? Is everyone healthy?"

"It's nothing like that," I assured her. "I found my biological father."

Gina was standing in our living room. She walked slowly into the kitchen and just stared at me, speechless.

I gave them the rundown on Ancestry DNA, and the past two months of talking with Edward.

Matt was sitting at our kitchen table. "Wow! This is incredible! Congratulations!"

Congratulations. Another word I hadn't thought of to describe all of this.

I showed Gina his photo on my phone.

"That's crazy. You look just like him."

"I know."

"Does he have any kids?"

"Three boys. They don't know about any of this yet." Informing Gina of my news wasn't like telling Rachel or any of my friends. I had been through it a few times now, I had the motions down, knew what words to say, but there was something missing with telling Gina: excitement. With everyone else, I felt optimistic, like my chances of a relationship with these people was promising. Telling Gina was sobering. It was like revealing a dream to her, one I didn't want to wake up from, but I had and, now, in real life, it just wasn't as pleasant as the dream had been. In real life, it was becoming more and more like a piece of fiction, something that would never come true.

Gina took a breath. "Does Mom know?"

"No, not yet, but I'm going to tell her."

Gina bit her lip. She hated confrontation. Gina would try to avoid any sign of a rocking boat. She liked things calm and harmonious. "I wonder how she is going to react."

I shrugged. "I don't know, but I'm telling her soon."

"Text me a couple of hours before you tell her."

"Why?" I asked.

"I want to be sure I don't talk to her that day."

APRIL 30, 2017

Two Sundays passed since Easter and I really, really didn't want to be the one to call. I checked my phone at ten, at eleven, at twelve. *Shit.* I was going to have to be the one to call. I went down to my office and readied myself. This would most likely be our last conversation. I took a few deep breaths and cussed him out for not calling me first. I picked up my iPhone when it suddenly rang. It was Edward.

"Thank you," I whispered to no one in particular. I answered. "Hello?"

Edward sounded mellow, easy to talk to again. He was at home, but he noted that Bev was out. He had a lower timbre in his voice, which gave me a false sense of security. I wanted to trust him, but I didn't.

143

I talked to him a little about work, explaining the things I had been teaching the past two weeks. I attempted to bring up the girls, but he moved quickly off that subject. He told me about Bev's troubles and how she didn't want Edward to talk to his cousin Jerry Wachtel ever again because he had matched me on Ancestry. She was certain Jerry was telling his entire family. "She is still screaming and throwing the remote at the TV every time Ancestry runs a commercial, which feels like happens every hour."

"Maybe you guys should listen to the radio more," I suggested.

Edward chuckled but it sounded sad.

I cleared my throat and got serious. "Maybe you guys need to see a therapist or a counselor."

"I told her I wanted to go see one," Edward confessed. "I told her we needed to go together but she refuses."

"She does?"

"Yeah, she said what's the point in paying for a therapist when they end up telling you exactly what you want to hear anyway?"

Bev was anti-everything when it came to any positive light that could be shed my way.

"You still want to meet?" Edward suddenly asked.

This was a surprise. I steadied myself. "Yes, I would like that."

"Well," he shuffled some papers, "I was looking it up and the halfway point between me and you is a town called Barry. Do you know it?"

"No," I said, "But I can find it."

"Okay, I'm thinking noon next Wednesday. Would that work for you?"

Next Wednesday or this Wednesday? "May 3 or May 10?" I clarified.

Edward paused. "May 10."

Lucky for me, I would be done with teaching the Friday before. "Yes, that will work for me. I got it on my calendar. Where would you like to meet?"

"There's a couple of bar and grills there. I'll call you next Monday and go over the details with you—"

"Sounds good." I interrupted and tried not to kick myself for sounding too excited.

"First I need to ask Bev if it's okay. You know, check with the Powers that Be."

My excitement plummeted. I evened my breathing out. My eyes closed. "Okay," I said. There was nothing I could do. I knew he had to check with Bev. She was his wife. I felt Wednesday slipping through my fingers just as fast as I could say, "Let me know what she says."

"I will. I'll call on Monday."

"Monday."

"Right," he agreed. "Monday. Or Tuesday."

I nodded. "Either day is fine. I look forward to it."

There was a pause and then he replied in an upbeat voice, "Yeah. I'm looking forward to it, too."

TWENTY-SIX

I like difficult women. I always have, I always will. There is something about a difficult woman that I am attracted to, whether it's in business or love. At work, I would rather collaborate with a difficult woman because she often brings a lot to the table. A difficult woman has inventive ideas, she's driven, and she's focused. While other people may complain about these types of women and avoid working with them, I welcome it. I thrive under the pressure they bring to the project.

I live with four difficult women. They all possess their own strengths, which drive me crazy in different ways. But I wouldn't want it any other way. Their ability to be difficult—to challenge me in everyday tasks—keeps me sharp, keeps me on my toes, and guarantees me a lifetime of never being bored. I am open to and accept the demands of a difficult woman. Of course, with this, I do not hold back as I am also difficult and bring one hundred percent to the table.

That's where we dance.

Bev tested my patience. Or, should I say, what I was being told about Bev tested my patience. There were times I wanted to tell Edward, *"Forget the lunch with you, let me meet with Bev."* She was the one I needed to clear the hurdle. She seemed so fearful of my family, of who we were telling, of the possibility of what was to come next. According to everything I was being told, Bev was irrationally hysterical with fear . . . of me.

Me.

I wasn't a scary person. There are certain things a guy knows about himself. Could I be an asshole? Sure. Were there times I said something I wished I could take back? Yeah. But, ninety-five percent of the time, I lived my life true to those around me. I am an open book. You ask me a question, I'm going to look you in the eyes and give you the honest answer. I have worked hard in my profession, with my students, in my art, for my family, in my marriage, with my girls, for my parents, my sisters, my in-laws, our extended family and friends — to be the best I could be for each one of those people.

And deep down, I knew Bev had done those things, too. I was certain that she was a good person. I was not scared of her. I wasn't scared of Edward, and I definitely did not shy away from our situation, as it unfolded. I wanted to embrace everything — all the truths and all the faults — and move forward. If we could figure a way to do that, it would be on the other side of all this bullshit, where we could all find peace and acceptance.

But how do you tell all that to a person who won't talk to you? How do you explain the years of longing to know who you were and where you came from? How do you articulate the grueling hours of painful research and work trying to find one nameless face?

I was the product of Bev's husband and another woman. Here I was, undeniable that I belonged to Edward. Bev's first instinct was to push me away, delete the email, hide in secrecy, and never tell anyone about me.

Bev could do all those things and pretend that I didn't exist, but the thing was, I did. No matter what she did to ignore my presence, I was already here. Now she just wanted me to go away.

When my mother was pregnant with me, she was shamed. After I arrived, she was shunned by many of those who were supposed to support her—the high school administration, her friends, and her own family. I was a shame baby, born during a time where it was normal to treat young, unwed mothers like that. Now forty-six years later, I still carry the burden of my mother's shame.

Deep down, I think I thought if I found my bio-father, I would get truthful answers. Maybe he would offer me something that would provide a release of some of the guilt I carried. Instead, what I inherited was the burden of Edward's shame. He was clear and concise, and he didn't have any problems hiding the fact that he thought I was a mistake. While I was pleased to find that I was half of him, he was mortified. And so was Bev.

It was a struggle to find my torch in this world, to radiate and shine my light, while wading through the darkness of my biological parents' disgrace.

It wasn't my actions. It was my mother's. It was Edward's. Whether it was one night or two dates—there was a moment where something crazy happened and nine months later I was born. I was an inconvenient truth born because Edward Schneyder and my mother had sex. And now, what did I want? More than I thought I did. I wanted a friendship with this man. With my half-siblings. Hell, I wanted a friendship with Bev.

For all that to happen, though, Bev had to be on board.

TWENTY-SEVEN

The last thing Edward had said to me was that he would talk to me the Monday or Tuesday before we were to meet.

He didn't call for our regular Sunday chat.

He didn't call on Monday.

"I bet he doesn't call," I said to Amy. "Bev isn't going to let him meet up with me and he doesn't have the balls to call and tell me."

"He'll call," Amy assured me.

Tuesday came and Edward called around noon. I was instantly relieved and was strangely lifted by his voice. It was as if twelve-year-old me suddenly swelled to the surface and I wanted to yell out, *"He called!"*

Edward, however, got right down to it. "Michael, I'm calling about tomorrow. I talked with Bev and she isn't feeling good about this. I worked it out with her, though, and I can still meet you but I can't meet you at noon. I have to change the time to two."

I wrote it down. "Two is good. Where should we meet?"

"Bev doesn't want me meeting you at a bar so ... are you familiar with the Flying J's Truck Stop in Welby?"

"No, I'm not."

"Okay, well, it's kind of new. It's straight out on I-80. You can't miss it. It's halfway between you and me."

"I will find it," I assured him. "I will see you there at 2pm. Tomorrow."

"Okay."

We hung up and I stared at what I had written. The Flying J's Truck Stop. I grew up near a truck stop, which had a café attached to it. My parents often stopped there for dinner with us kids. I hoped this was the same kind of place, where Edward and I could grab a piece of pie and a coffee. Or something.

Later in the evening, Amy and I Googled the truck stop. "There doesn't seem to be a café but there's an Arby's," she said helpfully. "You guys can share some curly fries and a shake."

I nodded but I already felt defeated. With Bev at the wheel, Edward and I were never going to have that beer.

MAY 10, 2017

There have been no words invented by the English language to describe how nervous I was the next day. The first time meeting Edward, at the DNA Lab, I was anxious and thought I was going to pass out but this was like an out-of-body experience. I was watching myself drive, as I took the exit, as I turned left, then right, then... where?

The Flying J's was fairly large. I wandered in and noticed it was a gas station/gift shop of odd items you can only buy at roadside venues. Kids toys, bumper stickers, hats, pocketknives, a Vikings helmet—*Ooh!* I picked it up. I always wanted one of these! But not for $69.95. Bummer. I put it back.

I peeked around but didn't notice Edward anywhere. I walked up and down the aisles, pretending to be interested in a rack of t-shirts. I pulled one out that said, "Is this Heaven? No, it's Iowa." I recognized the quote from the movie *Field of Dreams*, which was filmed in Iowa. My mind quickly flashed to the last scene of the movie where Kevin Costner realizes he built a baseball field in his cornfield so his dead father could return to him and they could play a game of catch.

I shoved the shirt back in the rack and kept walking. The Arby's was attached to the store so I ventured in there. No Edward. I decided this was the best place we could meet. I selected a booth in front of a large window and slid in, watching intently as cars pulled in and out.

I checked my phone. It was 2:10pm. He was ten minutes late. I thought about ordering a soda when I got a text: *Where are you?*

Edward. I glanced around but didn't see him. I texted back: *Inside the Arby's.*

Come across the street. I'm at the Kum & Go, sitting in my car.

I bit off a cuss word. *Ok.*

I exited Arby's and drove across the street. The minute I pulled into the parking lot, I noticed him. He drove his Buick this time, an Encore. I parked next to him and got out. He stayed in his car and rolled down the window. "Get in."

What the hell was this? Edward was ninety miles away from Lawrence and he wasn't able to be seen with me in public for fear someone would recognize him sitting with me?

I opened the door, ignoring my mother's sudden voice in the back of my head, *"Don't get in a car with strangers."* I sat down in the passenger seat. Edward was smoking, his window cracked open as he flicked ashes outside. "I figure this is as good a place as any. It's more private in here."

Son of a bitch! I couldn't believe this shit! This was our meeting place? Outside a gas station in his fucking car? This is where we have to talk, when there's a perfectly good Arby's across the street from us?

I smiled. "Sure. This is fine." I removed my sunglasses.

"Hold on. Let me get a good look at you," Edward said as he took his sunglasses off. He looked me up and down. "I don't see any family resemblance."

I raised my eyebrows. "It might be time to get your eyes examined, then."

Edward's face broke out into a grin. "I was just joking," he said. "You've got the Schneyder nose. You're mine."

I sat up taller.

"Before we begin, Bev has one rule and that is I'm not allowed to talk about our sons," he said.

Allowed. I ignored the word. "Okay. Understood."

"Bev is still having a difficult time. She did not want me to come here today."

I glanced out my window. I wondered if Bev was out in the parking lot, watching our every move. Or maybe Edward was recording us.

"She pulls out your letter and reads it twice a day," he said. It took me a moment to realize he was talking about the initial letter that I had written. It felt so long ago. "She's obsessed with the part where you wrote that you don't want to disrupt our life and you're not looking for anything."

"I'm not," I lied. Those words were true, when I wrote the letter. But as each day passed by, I found that I was wanting more. Now I wanted a friendship. With all of them.

"She keeps telling me I can walk away at any time."

"You can," I assured him. Of course he could. He could do anything that he wanted. But so far, he had chosen to stay.

"Are you religious?" Edward asked.

I had to give the words a minute to sink in. I was preoccupied with studying his face. The similarities really were spooky. "I'm not," I replied honestly. "I grew up in the Christian Church, just a few doors down from my house. When I was five, I was playing in my front yard and heard singing, so I wandered in and I liked it so much, I went there until I was sixteen. Then they built a new church a few miles away and moved locations. I didn't have a car to get there so I stopped going. Today, I'm somewhere between an agnostic and an atheist." I wasn't sure what kind of reaction that would get so I added, "But I'm married to a Catholic. We're in a mixed marriage."

"What about your kids?"

"When Amy and I were married, I agreed that we would raise them Catholic. We've been open with them as far as religion and made it clear that they can make whatever choice their heart leads them to."

He nodded. "I was raised Lutheran. I haven't gone to church in a long time." He took a long drag on his cigarette. "You know, Lutherans and Catholics are not supposed to talk to each other. Historically, they don't get along."

"Well, time changes a lot of things," I said. "If a Catholic and an atheist can make it work, I'm sure there's hope for the Lutherans."

"My brothers and sisters are divided. Half of us are Lutherans, the other half are atheists."

"It sounds like my family would fit in pretty well, then."

He nodded. He smiled. The smile disappeared. "Bev is freaking out. She and I have been married about forty-three years." He paused. "How long did you say you and your wife have been married?"

I shrugged. "Close to a hundred. I kind of lost count."

Edward laughed. "Bev's mother is ninety and she's *very* religious."

"Is she?"

"Yeah," Edward continued. "She believes the good things in life are blessings from God and the bad things are curses." He lifted his eyes to mine. "So she can never, ever find out about you."

"Because I would be considered a curse."

Edward huffed a laugh. "Oh, shit, yeah. A big one."

Curse = bad. Curse = me. Bad = me. Understood. "You have nothing to worry about on my side. I would never tell your mother-in-law any of this."

"I'm sure you won't, but people talk. Bev doesn't want it to get back to her. It would be devastating." Edward then went on about how he and Bev had recently placed her mother in a nursing home and how this was upsetting to Bev, which was the start of the next fifteen-minute rant about Bev. "She won't let me go anywhere. Shit, I can't go to the grocery store without her trailing after me. I have to show her receipts from the golf club to prove that I was there. Do you know how embarrassing it is to ask for a receipt from a guy you've known for your entire life just to prove to your wife that you were golfing? Bev used to be just fine with me doing whatever I wanted, whenever I wanted, but not now. Now I have a full-time babysitter."

I shot another look out the window, giving a quick canvass of the area.

"I know you're my son."

My head turned back his way.

"I have decided that if anyone asks me, I am not going to deny you. I accept the truth. You are mine. But, Bev ... she just can't get there. She knows she is behaving badly. Just the other day, she told me that she knows she shouldn't feel this way, but she just does."

"Well, that could be a positive step in the right direction," I said.

He shook his head. "Maybe." He smoked, flicked ashes.

I tried to change the subject. "I'm sure you've had time to have me checked out," I said.

"What? Oh, yeah, sure. I've had you checked out."

"So, you know that I'm not a criminal. I've never done drugs, I've never been busted by the cops, and I've never been sued. I work hard and take good care of my family. I'm not perfect. I probably drink a little too much sometimes, but I like to have a good time. I've been fortunate enough to live a good life. I don't want any money or anything from you. The only thing I'm looking for is a friendship." I watched for a reaction but didn't see one. "I don't ever want to be put in a Will, and I don't need a chair at the table on holidays. I don't need a father because I already have one. But I would like the chance to get to know you better. My hope is that we can become friends."

Edward seemed to be taking in my words. He swallowed a couple of times. "I don't know if Bev will ever get there. She's difficult."

"I like difficult women. I'm married to one and I'm raising three of them."

Edward lit another cigarette. "This whole thing has gotten me in a lot of hot water with Bev. Maybe it wouldn't be so bad and I would feel like I deserved some of it, if I had ever gotten a piece of ass from your mother, but I didn't get the chance. I never even had sex with her."

My ears were burning. I felt my body heat up. I steadied my breathing and attempted to keep my face blank. Edward's mouth was still moving but I was stuck on: *Piece of ass.* He was talking about my seventeen-year-old mother and referring to her as a *piece of ass?* This dickhead was still trying to sell his stupid, no-sex story to me? Why? I could only assume it was because it was the story he was telling Bev and he had to make it stick. Which meant he had to drill it home for me, too.

"Have you told your mother you found me?"

"No," I said.

His mouth twitched. "I would appreciate it if you wouldn't."

I wanted to think of something brilliant to say to lessen his anxiety, but I wasn't going to make a promise I couldn't keep. I understood that his request was most likely Edward's way to control the narrative—if I didn't tell my mother I had found him, he could tell me anything he wanted—but if Edward and I had a shot at a future,

I wasn't sure how we could do that, open and honestly, without my mom knowing. She didn't have to be part of the relationship between Edward and me, but I would have to come clean with her about what I had done.

Edward threw his cigarette out the window. "I don't need your mother to know until I figure out how to deal with Bev. I don't need two crazy women at my throat."

Okay, I was done with this conversation. It didn't matter what we talked about, everything circled back to Bev. It was clear that moving forward was not an Edward-Michael problem, it was an Edward-Bev problem and I couldn't get in the middle any more than I already was.

"How about we take the summer off?" I suggested. "You and I take a break from talking and give Bev a few months to see if she can be more accepting of the situation. Since I've found you, everything has moved very fast. Personally, I am a bit overwhelmed by it all. I'm sure she feels that way, too. Maybe it's time to pump the brakes."

Edward liked that idea. "Three months off."

"Yeah," I said. "Take some time to let things absorb."

"Okay, well, it's May so . . . August?"

"Right. Unless, of course, you would like me to send you a Father's Day card?"

"Oh, Jesus! Christ! Don't do that!" he exclaimed. "Please do not send me a Father's Day card!"

I chuckled. "I won't, but I have a ton of great ideas for one."

Then he looked at me and read the joke behind my eyes. He broke out in a grin and we both laughed.

TWENTY-EIGHT

It was time to tell my mother.

Keeping the secret that I had found Edward from my mom had gone on long enough. With every passing day, I felt as if I was somehow cheating on my mom and I knew if I wanted to honestly live my truth in the open, then I needed to let her in on my discovery.

Two days after meeting with Edward, I drove to my childhood home in Altoona and found both of my parents there. *Good*, I thought. *Two birds, one stone.*

It took thirty minutes of small talk before I made my move. I was nervous to start. The past times I had brought this subject up, it ended with my mother in tears. It was difficult knowing that sharing something so exciting and momentous in my life was, in turn, something that might crush her.

I started with, "There's something I need to talk to both of you about."

My dad had been meandering around the living room, rambling on about politics, when he came to a complete stop. My mom was already sitting in a dining room chair. She placed her hands on her knees. They were within an arms distance from one another.

"First, I want you to know that I love you both very much," I hated that I had to start it out this way. Of course I loved them, but for some reason people's minds always go to bad places with big news. I wanted them to know that no matter what I was going to tell them, that my love for them was unchanged. "I found my biological father," I announced. I kept my voice calm, smooth, and confident.

Neither of them said a word. Their facial expressions didn't change. It was like I hadn't spoken at all.

"Did you hear me?" I asked. They remained still. "I found my biological father." Louder and slower, that time.

"No, you didn't," my mom said.

"Yeah, I did."

They were taken aback. Quietly, they exchanged a look with each other. "How?" My mother again.

"I took an AncestryDNA test. Do you know what that is?"

They shook their heads.

So, for the hundredth time, I launched into my story about the spit tube, the waiting, the close-family match, the research, contacting Louisa, narrowing it down to the two brothers, writing who I thought was my bio-father and that he had come to Des Moines and we had taken a paternity test. "Ninety-nine-point-nine-nine percent positive."

My parents were stunned.

"What . . . what's his name?" My mother asked.

"Edward Schneyder," I replied.

She blinked. "Say it again."

"Edward Schneyder," I repeated.

"Ed," she said, like a lightbulb went off. "Ed." She nodded. "So, you've met him?"

"Twice."

Again, my parents looked at each other.

"What does he say about things?" she asked.

I shrugged. "Edward and his wife are having a hard time with it."

"He wasn't married when you were…" my dad spoke up, cutting off his own sentence.

"No!" my mom yelled.

I shook my head. "He wasn't married then, but they have been married for more than forty years and she's … not happy."

"I bet," my mom said.

"You think her reaction is normal?" I asked.

"Of course, it is. You're disrupting their family. I would be unhappy if I were her."

I frowned. "You would be unhappy if Dad found out he had another son who was born four years before you got married?"

My mom thought about it. "Yes."

I cupped my hands over my mouth. "Mom, you had a son four years before you and dad got married!"

She huffed. "That's different."

I shook my head. "The only difference is timing."

My mother took a couple of breaths, like she was trying to clear her head. "I just don't understand why you would ever want to contact him. What's the point?"

What's the point? Five minutes in and this was not how I wanted this conversation to go. I felt it dangerously dip toward the crying zone. I needed to fix this. Fast. "Because I'm half of him," I answered. "You know that I have wanted this my entire life. I've always wanted to know who he is. You know how much this has bothered me." I stared hard at her. "You know."

My mom didn't say anything but my dad suddenly blurted out, "I thought when you said you had some news you were going to tell us that Rosie was pregnant."

I frowned. "What? No." I looked from him to her. "I found my dad!" Why I chose to use that word, I didn't know. I hadn't used it before this moment, but it just slipped out.

"Hey, hey!" My dad shouted. "Just wait a minute!"

"I'm sorry," I said. "I didn't mean that."

My mom put her hands up. "Why don't we just call him Ed?"

I nodded. My dad nodded.

"Ed, the sperm donor," she laughed.

I didn't.

My mom sighed. "Do you have a picture of him?"

I brought up Facebook and showed her. She shook her head. "He doesn't look familiar."

"Really?"

"I don't remember him."

"No?" I showed her a family photo from the 1980s when Edward was younger. My mom took the phone out of my hand and studied it.

"No," she said. "Does he have any kids?"

"Three. They're all boys."

"What do they think?"

"They don't know about me yet. He and his wife aren't telling them right now." I omitted the part where Edward said they never would. "Edward and I are taking the summer off from speaking to see if his wife can get used to the idea that I exist."

"Does he live in Des Moines?"

"No. Lawrence."

She shook her head. "Where is that?"

I told her.

"I've been through Lawrence before," my dad chimed in. "It's a very nice town."

"I'm sure it is."

"They had that big flood go through a few years ago," he continued.

"That's right."

He thought a moment. "I know a couple of people from around there."

162

Before I could inquire into who they may be, my mom asked, "Does Amy know?"

"Absolutely."

"And the girls?"

"Yes."

This peaked my dad's interest. "The girls know? Really? You told them?"

"Sure," I said, like it was no big deal.

"What did they say?" he asked.

"They're excited but we've told them to be cautious. They have a lot to absorb right now. Like me, they are genetically affected by this, too." I paused and added, "If he's open to it, they would like to meet him someday."

"I mean, what did they say when they found out that I'm not their biological grandfather?"

"Oh, they've known for a while."

This surprised my father and, to be honest, I gave him this information in a very casual way. I had no idea he was going to take it as hard as he did.

"They've known for a while?" He repeated slowly.

I nodded. "I told each of them when they were around ten years old."

He quietly did the math in his head. "So Rosie has known for almost ten years that I'm not her ... *biological* grandfather?"

"Yes," I said.

He sat down. My mother sat down next to him and they both gazed out into space, looking like I had driven a semi through their living room. I was at a loss of words at their reaction. Had they really thought that I would continue to keep their secret buried? That I wouldn't tell my children that twenty-five percent of their DNA was unknown? And had they also just expected Amy to carry the burden of keeping the secret, too? And her family? And our friends?

I panicked. "They know who their grandfather is, Dad," I said. "It's you. You're the one who has been here, you're their connection, not him. But they also don't know twenty-five percent of their own genetic makeup. And I know that doesn't sound like a lot, to someone who knows solely where he comes from, but they have the right to know. This is important to them. It's important to me. I haven't known where fifty percent of *me* comes from and I'm just starting to get that chance." I waited for a response but neither one of them said anything. "What would you do if you were me? Wouldn't you want to know?"

It was quiet. Then my dad nodded. "Yeah. Yeah, I would. I understand why you are doing this, Miguel. I do." My father had terms of endearment for all of his kids, one of mine was Miguel. "It's a lot to take in, that's all. I'm just very surprised."

I looked at my mom. She let out a great sigh. "Well, I feel like fifty pounds has been lifted off my shoulders." She laughed. "I can't believe you found him! You should be a private investigator!"

"Amy helped me," I confessed.

"So, are we the first ones that you've told?"

I hesitated. Her question was sensitive because I knew they wanted me to say "Yes." They didn't just *want* to be the first ones that I told, they *needed* to be. I understood that. Years of knowing that everyone in my life knew my secret years before I did was hurtful. I didn't want them to feel that kind of pain. I didn't want to tell them that I had talked it over with my friends and in-laws and that I had already told both of my sisters. I looked my mother in the eyes and said, "Yes, you guys are the first ones to know."

You know, like a liar would say.

She nodded. "That's good."

My parents and I stared at each other for a few seconds, just letting the words and feelings wash over us.

"I don't want to see him," my mother said. "You can do whatever you want—you have my full blessing—but I don't want to see him. Ever."

I nodded. "Okay. That's fine." I thought about Edward and where we were at this moment. "I doubt that our relationship will ever get to that point, anyway."

"And I want this to stay off of Facebook." My mom again.

Fuck, no. I wasn't going to continue to be a secret anymore. I could and would tell anyone I wanted in any form I desired. I had been living my entire life keeping this part of my life in the shadows when the only reason I did it was to spare my mother's feelings. That was her shame speaking, not mine. I didn't have to live in whatever fucked up world her brain was telling me that I needed to. I wasn't a bastard. I wasn't a shame baby. I was finally taking hold of who I was, and I could own it anyway I chose.

I nodded and, as usual, tiptoed around the subject. "It won't be on Facebook, for now."

"Let me see a picture of him," my dad put his hand out. I realized when I gave my mom my phone, I had left my dad out. I pulled up two photos and passed my cell over. My dad looked at them and nodded. "Yeah, he's definitely the one." He handed the phone back. "Man, this is deep. I bet you've been stressed out."

I chuckled. "You have no idea."

"You know, I'm ... I'm happy for you."

He was sincere and I believed him. Like my mom, I felt a huge relief. It was oddly liberating.

"I love you guys," I repeated. I hugged my dad and then I hugged my mom. They told me that they loved me, too.

We all sat down, each of us quiet, but our thoughts were loud. My mom cleared her throat. "What was his last name again?"

"Schneyder. Edward Schneyder."

She said it, almost a whisper to herself. "Schneyder." She laughed. "I knew it was weird. I could have never remembered that last name. I can barely remember it now."

TWENTY-NINE

The evening after meeting with Edward, Amy was on Facebook and saw my second cousin-match, Jerry Wachtel, had posted some old family photos. Amy posed the question, "Jerry, who are these people?" Within fifteen minutes of her post, I received a text from Edward telling me that she had to take the post down because Bev had seen it and was freaking out. I spoke with Amy, who was in tears for her misstep, and she immediately removed her comment.

I texted Edward. *Amy feels badly. She has taken down her comment. It won't happen again. We are sorry for any bad feelings caused.*

Edward texted back. *If you want this to work, you need to get a grip on your woman.*

After a couple of hours, Amy sat down with me outside. "You know, if Bev can't handle me asking an innocent question on your second cousin's Facebook page, she will never be okay with you sitting across a table from one of her sons."

I ignored her comment, but I felt it. All I could do now was wait the summer out. The ball was in their court. It was their move and if I wanted to stay in the game, I had to play by their rules.

One week after talking with my parents, my mom called on a sunny day. Mother Nature was shining down, letting us know that summer was indeed on the way. My mom sounded as carefree as the weather. She wanted me to know that since our conversation, she felt incredible. "I never realized that I needed to know, too," she beamed. "Just knowing his name, being able to assign it to him in my head has released a lot of guilt."

"That's awesome," I said.

"I talked to Rachel today. She said you told her about Edward."

"Yeah, I told her and Gina," I said. I didn't mention when I had told them.

"I was talking to Rachel about when I met Edward and she said I needed to call you and go over my story again because apparently it's different than Edward's."

I let out a held breath. "Okay." I searched the kitchen and grabbed a pen. "Go ahead."

Her version was the same story she told me back in 1992. Walking off of Grand—he pulled up on a motorcycle—they drove around—he took her back to his house—they had sex there—it was her first time—he took her home—he got her number—he was the one to call again—it was a month later—he came over—they went on a drive—he returned her home and no one was there—they had sex—he left—she didn't hear from him for a couple of months—when he called, she told him she was pregnant—he said he would come over and he never showed. Then she asked, "What does he say happened?"

I disclosed Edward's story to her of how she showed up at the house that night, she was a friend of a girl that one of the guys was dating, how she was kicked out of the house by her boyfriend, that she slept the night with the other guy, and how he woke up to a naked surprise in the morning, but they never had sex, his underwear was on the entire time, that she fell asleep on the sofa, he got up and went to work, and when he came back, she was gone and he never heard from her again.

My mom was quiet for about three seconds and then she laughed and she laughed. And then laughed some more. "Oh, my God!" she laughed. "That's hilarious!" When she caught her breath, she said, "Mike, none of my friends dated anyone who lived with him." She laughed. "And I didn't even get pregnant with you at that house. I got pregnant the second time Ed and I had sex. When we were at Grandma and Grandpa's house. That's where you were conceived." She started laughing. "His underwear was on. ..." And more laughter. "His wife believes this?"

I shrugged. "I guess so."

My mom quieted down. "His wife doesn't believe that. Nobody would believe that story."

"As far as I know, she's believing it," I said.

"Then his wife's problem isn't completely with you, Mike. Her biggest problem is the fact that her husband is lying to her and she knows it and she's stuck standing there, knowing that if people knew that stupid story he's telling that they would also know that she was standing by a fool."

I didn't say anything.

"And he's lying to you, too. Just like he lied to me. He's lying to you."

Of course he was. Why wouldn't I expect him not to? From the moment I was born, people had lied to me. Instead of being honest and having my mother tell me at a young age, *"I don't know who your biological father is, but this man loved you so much that he wanted to keep you as his own ..."* she chose to ignore the question mark hanging over my head. My entire family did.

Why would I expect my biological father to tell me the truth?

I thanked my mom for her call and for going into more detail about when and where I was conceived. I was calm but my mind was racing—Was she right? Was I conceived at my grandparents' house or was it in that house that Edward rented? Did it matter? Either way, I was here.

My mother seemed sure of herself, though. "It was the late sixties and early seventies . . . it was a different time."

I hung up the phone and closed my eyes. I was getting really tired of hearing that phrase *It was a different time.* I'm sure it was. Times change but people stay pretty much the same. They know when wrong is wrong and right is right. No matter what decade they are in.

* * *

That night Amy and I took a break and went to see Hamilton at the Des Moines Civic Center. I had been excited to see the show. Amy surprised me with the tickets and as the lights went down, the chords of violins, pianos, and drums thumped against my chest.

The actors took stage and the first words from the musical were sung by Aaron Burr, claiming Hamilton was a bastard and a son of a whore. I lost my breath for a moment. Every move I made, it was there, taunting me. I was never going to escape this.

THIRTY

Shortly after my visit with Edward and the talk with my parents, Amy and I received an email from Catey's Language Arts teacher. She had assigned her class the task of writing a persuasive speech. While many students chose to write letters to their congressman about legalizing marijuana or to Mark Zuckerberg about where he could spend some of his Facebook money, Catey's approach was more personal. It was to Edward.

Her teacher wrote in the email: *I have requested Catey's speech be published in the student newspaper. Although I do not know anything more about your family's situation than what Catey has written, I do want to encourage you to make sure Catey mails a copy of her speech to Edward. When Catey read the letter to the class, I broke down and cried as did many of the students. This man needs to hear this letter.*

And so, two weeks after talking with Edward, I broke my pact of taking a break over the summer and sent him Catey's A+ paper:

Catey Blair, 8th Grade
Persuasion Letter
Language Arts, Fourth Period
May 26, 2017
Audience: 1

Dear Edward,

Hi. My name is Catey Blair. My Dad is Michael Blair. I am writing you today to talk to you about your situation with my family. I know that your situation focuses more with my Dad but I feel like behind my Dad, there are me and my sisters and that we have a voice in this situation, too.

I want you to know that my parents have spoken freely about you and your situation with my Dad. When my sisters and I were each about ten years old, my Dad told us that our Papa Craig was not our biological grandpa so we have all known that you have existed in the world for a while. Over the years I can remember my parents talking openly about finding you and wondering who you were. You have always been someone we talked about, even when we didn't have a name to call you. So you've always kind of been part of our lives and our family.

When we found out that my Dad had finally found you, my sisters and I felt relieved and happy. Then our Mom and Dad explained to us that you were not sure if you wanted to move ahead getting to know my Dad. They explained to us that sometimes this kind of news isn't always happy for everyone and the shock of everything can be too much. Our parents told us we had to be patient and give you time to get used to the news that my Dad was in the world. My Mom explained to us that it was probably difficult for you to even think about my sisters and me because you were in shock about my Dad.

My sisters and I still feel like we have a say in this, too. If we could talk to you, we would tell you that we are excited to meet you one day. We want to tell you that we have always wondered about you and because we've talked about you for so long, we are excited to get to know you. I think you would like us. You would like my sister Rosie because she is so good with people. She talks and talks. When she was little, people nicknamed her Princess Blah Blah because she talks so much. Now that she's older, she is someone who is easy to talk to and she's really sweet. You would like my sister Jill because she's so funny. She's funny without knowing that she's funny, which is the best kind of funny. From the couple of pictures that we have seen from your family, I can tell you that both my sisters look like your family. It's weird because my parents always knew Rosie looks like my Dad but no one really knew who Jill looked like. She looks like a lot of your people, which is good to know. I look like my Mom's side of the family so I don't look like you very much.

I hope one day you will want to come over and have a cookout with my family. My Dad is great on the grill. He makes yummy food and my Mom is an amazing baker. She can make you a delicious dessert. My sisters and I could play you a song. We all play the piano and Jill plays the trumpet and I play the drums. We all like to sing and we are very musical. Do you like music? Do you play an instrument? We also are really good artists. Do you draw or paint? I wonder what things you like to do.

My Mom says that every person has a light inside of them that helps them move forward in life. She says it helps us get through tough times. She explained to me that when I was born, half my light was ignited by her and half my light was ignited by my Dad and that together they started my flame. She said as I move through life, I will meet people who will continue to add fuel to my light and that in the end, I will hopefully feel happy and warm. I want you to know that my sisters and I all have very bright lights. So I know that the light we received from my Dad was full of good, which means he must have gotten some of that from you.

I hope over the summer you are able to find a resolution with yours and my Dad's situation and I hope that in the end you choose to want to have a friendship with him because then we can have a friendship, too! If you are in, my sisters and I are all in, too.

Your Friend (and Granddaughter),
  Catey Blair

THIRTY-ONE

The summer felt like it lasted for six months instead of three. I am sure the phrase "Time flies when you're having fun" is true but when you're not having fun, time drags. Three months is a very long time when you are waiting to see if a person—your parent—is going to accept or reject you.

I had the summer off from teaching but was working a side hustle at an advertising agency, which I had done for many summers in the past. It kept me busy, although my mind often drifted to Edward, wondering how things were going in Lawrence. I had exchanged an email with Louisa, letting her know about the arrangement between Edward and me. Louisa agreed taking the summer off could be a good thing, giving everyone some space and time to adjust to a possible new normal. She told me Edward was not one to rush into anything and that at the end of the three months, surely there would be new light shed on our situation. Louisa remained hopeful and optimistic. It was comforting.

I made two Father's Day cards. For the outside of my dad's, I designed a pack of soda cans, fireworks, and explosions. The inside said, "Out of all the Pops in the world, you're my favorite one." The second card I designed was for Edward. His was just a big, lone, sperm, swimming up a canal where a glowing, red egg was awaiting its arrival. The inside said, "Your pull-out game was weak as fuck."

I only sent the one to my dad.

Several weird things happened that summer.

People were starting to talk. We knew that this was already occurring but during the summer, the chatter increased. Two of Amy's cousins came forward and said they had connections to the Schneyders. One cousin, Carson, was married to Natalie. Her mother was Edward's cousin and she knew the Schneyders fairly well. One night, Natalie confided in Amy that she had invited her siblings over to see her new house. They started a bonfire and started drinking when Natalie let it slip to her family about me. This caused a flurry of excitement. Natalie passed around photos of us and talked us up. Natalie then contacted Amy and told her that she and her siblings were good friends with my half-brother Mark, and they felt that if Mark only knew about me, that he could help us solidify my relationship with Edward. If Mark knew, things could be better for all of us. All they needed was to have my permission and they would gladly approach Mark and talk to him.

That was a quick NO. Amy and I agreed that the only thing that could make our relationship with Edward worse was to tell one of their kids. We didn't want us or anyone else to be the ones to tell their boys. We wanted Edward and Bev to tell them.

Amy's other cousin, Darron, told her that he knew my Uncle Marty, the youngest of the family. They played football together in college and Darron had nothing but good things to say about Marty. He teased Amy that he might just tell Marty, but Amy assured me he was just joking. I put it in the back of my mind.

However, early in the summer, Amy and I reached out to Carolyn, the aunt who had sent me the Facebook message months prior. It was something I weighed heavily, but in the end, I really wanted another family member's opinion, and she had already willingly reached out.

My conversation with Carolyn was exactly what I had dreamed of in finding my biological family. She was warm, inviting, and excited. Carolyn talked easily about her childhood and her relationship with Edward and his boys. She talked about the struggles the family had experienced since their parents died. Like Louisa, she was optimistic that Edward would come around and would accept me into his family. She felt that when his boys found out that I existed, they would also be welcoming. She also sympathized with Bev's ambivalence.

"Honestly, if I were in her shoes, I would probably act the same way," Carolyn said. "I would have to get to a place where I could meet you and after that, I would make a decision on how to proceed."

"What would need to be done to get you to the point where you would talk to me?" I asked. I needed to break through that wall to Bev.

"I think it would take me a couple of months but in the end, I wouldn't be able to deny my husband his child. Especially if he were conceived before we were ever married. It would take some praying on my part but I would come to that conclusion. I'm sure I would." She laughed. "I hope I would. For Bev, I don't know. Time, yes, but I think the support of her boys would make the real difference." She smiled. "Just talking with you the little that I have, I can tell that you would get along well with your brothers."

Carolyn had been married for almost forty years. Her husband, Randy, had been married previously and had two children, whom Carolyn had a hand in raising. "They lived with us full-time since they were three and four years old," she said. "So I may be more liberal in my thinking since I have always been an active stepparent."

Lots of Edward's brothers and sisters had been married and divorced. Many of them were step-parents, one had adopted a previous child, like my dad had with me. Only three of the ten kids had never been divorced, one of them being Edward and, so, having a blended family was certainly not something that he or Bev ever anticipated they would have to face.

"She didn't sign up for this," Carolyn said. "I mean, we all say our vows—for better or for worse—but she didn't expect this. She never knew when she married her husband that he already had a three-year-old kid out there. And she certainly never thought forty-two years later that kid was going to show up on her doorstep."

Carolyn's image she painted of Edward's family was tight, and yet strained. The three boys were very different and each one had almost five years age difference between the next. With the oldest having legal problems and the middle son being the law, there were bound to be some hiccups along the way.

"It doesn't sound like Ozzie and Harriet," I said. Not that I expected it to be perfect.

"No," Carolyn agreed. "There's been some tough years."

She wanted to meet me and my family, which I was excited about. It would have to wait until after August, until the summer was over, and I knew which way Edward was leaning. I didn't want to cross too many lines and I had done that already with speaking to Carolyn. In many ways, I felt I had betrayed Edward and that came with guilt. On the other hand, I felt empowered. While I wanted to respect Edward's wishes, I was an adult and this woman was my biological aunt. She wanted to know me, she wanted to meet my family, and she didn't need to take the summer to figure that out. "I knew the minute I saw a picture of you—you are a Schneyder. I see Edward in you, I see my own son in you, and I see my dad in you! You belong to this family! I can't wait to meet you—if I could, I would jump in my car and drive to you right now! I can't wait to hug you!"

I blinked my eyes until they were dry. I cleared my throat twice.

"Likewise," was all I could manage.

Toward the end of summer, Amy's cousin Darron ramped up his teasing about telling Marty and Amy freaked out. "I think we may need to reach out to this guy before he hears about you from someone else."

Marty was a tough one to bring into this circle because, from what Louisa and Carolyn had told me, he and Edward were close. Amy offered to send him a private message on Facebook and things rolled from there. Marty was very kind and interested in knowing more about his newfound nephew. Amy had omitted which brother I belonged to, in case Marty didn't want to know. Marty asked to have a phone conversation with me and I obliged. This happened two weeks before I was to talk to Edward, and I thought maybe this was a good thing—getting a male perspective from one of Edward's brothers—may help navigate a positive outcome.

Speaking with Marty was enlightening. Like his sisters, he was surprised, but warm and welcoming. As we began the conversation, he said, "I don't need you to tell me which of my brother's is your father. I've looked at your Facebook page and I know it's Edward. You look just like him."

I smiled. It never got old hearing that I looked like a member of their family.

Marty was interested in where Edward and I were at this point. I gave him a brief synopsis of my journey. I explained how Ancestry DNA worked, matching to Louisa and Jerry Wachtel, reaching out to Louisa, the letter I had written to Edward, how he came down to do the paternity test with me, and how things had progressed and declined since then. I ended by telling him that Edward and I were on a break for the summer but in a couple of weeks, we would be talking again to see where things stood between us.

"Ed takes his time thinking things through," Marty told me. "If this is new information to him, it's going to take him a while to process."

I told Marty a simplified version of my mother's story and I also told him about Edward and his underwear story. Marty was quiet and then said, "Well, something had to have happened."

I laughed. "Right. I know. I don't want to discount Edward's story, but it seems a little far-fetched." I didn't want to say anything too harsh, that might scare Marty away. "I'm sure there are truthful parts in both stories."

Marty agreed. He opened up about his relationship with Edward. "He has helped me out more times than I can count. Through my life, he has been like a second father to me. I have followed his advice over any else's." Marty talked about being the baby of ten kids and his unique family dynamic, having fifteen years age difference between the oldest to him. "I get along with all of them," he proudly said. Then he paused and added, "Well, most of them."

"This summer, I've had one phone conversation with Louisa," I confessed. "And we have exchanged about four emails. I have also recently spoken to Carolyn as well."

"My sister Carolyn?"

"Yes."

"How does Carolyn know?"

"When I took the AncestryDNA test, I matched to your cousin Jerry Wachtel and I believe she found out through him and his sister."

Marty was quiet.

"From what I am understanding," I said slowly, "I'm pretty sure the news that Edward has another son is slowly trickling down through your family."

"Ed isn't going to like that," Marty piped in. "Don't talk to Carolyn. She's a crazy person and Jerry . . . just, don't talk to Jerry." He said it like it was an order.

"I haven't *spoken* to him," I told him. "We are friends on Facebook, and we have exchanged a few messages back and forth, but I haven't talked or met with him."

Marty paused. "Ed wouldn't like it if you talked to Jerry."

I blinked. "Edward knows I matched with Jerry," I explained. "He also can see that Jerry and I are Facebook friends. He's aware of that."

"Okay." Marty sighed. "Louisa is a good person to talk to. She's a vault. If you need to talk to someone, I would definitely lean on Louisa. She's a good ally and Edward trusts her."

I nodded. "Good to know." I jotted it down. *Louisa = Good.*

Marty was funny, he had a sharp sense of humor and made me feel at ease. I told him about Edward wanting to originally meet me for a drink and how he asked if I was a person who liked alcoholic drinks.

"Well, are you?" Marty teased.

"I drink vodka in the summer, whiskey in the winter and beer is fair game all year around."

"Me, too!" Marty exclaimed and I could feel the smile on the other side of the phone. "When I got the message from your wife," he said, "I almost had a heart attack because for a split second I thought you could be mine. But I was only ten so that eliminated me."

We laughed.

"Seriously, I have joked that one day, somebody might knock on my door, you know? So this information hit pretty close to home." Marty rattled on about how he was close to Edward's sons, especially Mark, the middle one. "As long as Edward is comfortable with bringing you into the family, the boys will be, too. But, Bev will never accept you," he said. "She will never allow you to walk into her house."

That was the problem, wasn't it? How could I be accepted by Edward and my half-brothers if Bev couldn't open that door to me?

"Even though they weren't married yet and I'm sure you were

conceived when Ed and Bev were broken up."

"Oh? They broke up?" I asked. This was something I hadn't heard until now.

"Yeah. They broke up before Ed took off for Oregon. They got back together after Ed left Des Moines, when he moved back to Lawrence. So you were conceived in the middle of all that."

I nodded and wrote down what Marty was saying. "So, they were on a break?"

"Oh, yeah. Bev actually dated another guy. One of Ed's friends."

"Interesting." I laughed.

"So," Marty's voice raised an octave. "Does Ed know that you are speaking to me?"

"No, he doesn't."

"Okay." Marty hesitated. "I'm not going say anything to him. I'm going to wait for him to come to me."

I chuckled. "You're going to be waiting a long time, then."

"Well," Marty began. I noticed they were all very careful with their words. "I don't want to be the one to tell Ed. In case it upsets him."

Huh. Both Louisa and Carolyn had said something similar. "It seems like you guys are afraid of him."

"Not afraid," Marty said quickly. "I just don't want to jeopardize my position with him."

Weird. I could honestly say that I never thought of myself as having a position with my sisters. They were mine, I was theirs. End of story. There was little they could do that would make me so angry that I would not continue to have a relationship with them.

"My silence is out of loyalty to him," Marty added.

Again, my mind went back to my conversation with Louisa. She had used the word "respect." Marty was using the word "loyal." Both were positive words, words that anyone would want to have associated to their name, but to what was Marty being loyal to? A secret that most likely Edward had held onto for forty-five years? Lying to his wife? To his sons? To his entire family? Being loyal to a man who abandoned my pregnant, teenage mother? Loyalty can take an ugly twist when you're blindly loyal to someone.

Again, I felt it. This wasn't about being loyal. This was about fear.

"Family means everything to Edward. So, you have that going for you," Marty added optimistically.

"Uh..." was all I had to contribute.

"I would like to meet you." I could hear his smile again. "I'm going to be in Ames for a Cyclone football game on September 28. It's a Thursday night game." I wrote it down. Marty lived in Wisconsin with his wife and daughter. From what he told me, it sounded like his daughter and my youngest, Jillian, were only one month apart in age. "I could meet you that afternoon, before the game."

"Sounds great," I said. Another possibility, another positive response from a family member.

We hung up and I jogged downstairs to fill in Amy and the girls about the conversation. My father-in-law, Leo, was visiting. He listened as I told everyone about my interaction with Marty.

Leo tilted his head. "So, your new dad isn't talking to you?"

I quickly explained to Leo about the agreement and how I would be calling Edward in the next couple of weeks to see where things stood between us.

Leo gave an animated shrug. "You know, if I could talk to that guy—your new dad—I would tell him from one grandfather to another... you're missin' out on three honeys." Leo's eyes landed hard on mine. "Those three girls are nothin' but sugar and they would love nothin' more than to love him." Leo sat back and counted on his fingers. "Rosie. Catey. Jillian... they got his blood in them but they also got mine and if he don't want them, he's the one missin' out. I would let him know that I will keep them and I will continue to love them twice as hard because he's not here to do his part." Leo looked away and then back at me once more. "You know, Amy is my daughter and she keeps this family in good shape. When people come into your life, Amy welcomes them with open arms and people gravitate to her because she's got charm." Leo pointed his finger at me. "But when people get closer in this family, they realize that you, Michael, you are the gift. And if I could tell your new dad anything, I would tell him for me, in my life, you have been one of the greatest gifts I ever got."

THIRTY-TWO

Not far into the summer we received an anonymous gift in the mail. It was a book written by a woman who grew up in Lawrence. The book is a memoir that follows the author's journey back to her hometown, after the devastating flood had swept through. The author spent the week in Lawrence, visiting old haunts and talking with former and current residents, many of whom she grew up with and attended high school.

Amy and I sat down and read through the chapters, taking in the visuals and we slowed down as the author wandered into the local golf course clubhouse to ask for a glass of wine. Sitting at the bar was Edward Schneyder, whom she graduated with in 1970. Working the bar was Edward's wife, Bev. They had a quick conversation, Edward immediately recognized the author and she talked briefly about their shared past.

The book skips from present time to past memories of her childhood and college years. She tours the soggy wreckage of the flood's path with a friend named Bruce Richter. They met up with yet another high school buddy, Teddy, and he triggers a memory from the author. We're transported in time to May 1970, when the author has just graduated from high school and she and Bruce go to visit Teddy, who lives in a house in Des Moines that he rents with four other guys from Lawrence. They all work in Des Moines, doing construction.

Amy and I stopped and looked at each other.

The book details the weekend the author experienced. The alcohol, the drugs, a girl showing up on the front lawn, accusing one of the guys of giving her gonorrhea. The author recalls how the visit made her physically ill and she threw up from everything she was given. Finally, after a night of booze and drugs, she passed out on the living room sofa. The next morning, she woke up still hazed and wanting nothing more than to leave. Bruce drove her the two hours back to Lawrence and dropped her off at home.

"Are you fucking kidding me?" I shouted. I read the lines again, over and over. The author names a few of the guys that lived in the house. Edward wasn't named but, from what I understood, he hadn't moved there yet. He would have just been getting to Oregon. He didn't go to Des Moines until the fall. But this was the house and these were the guys who lived there. I Googled the names listed. One guy was dead, Edward was right on that one. The others were alive. Edward's warning to me played on repeat in my head: *You can't talk to any of them. They're all dead.* Why would he say that? Did one of these men know something about me? Did he not want me seeking them out because one of them had kept his secret? When he made that phone call to my mom, and she told him she was pregnant, did he hang up and tell one of these guys? "He lied to me," I told Amy. *Don't let him lie to you,* my mom's voice popped in my head.

Someone wanted me to see this book and wanted me to know that not everyone in that house was dead.

But, what was I going to do? Get the phone numbers of three sixty-five-year-old men and call them to ask if they, by chance, remember the events that happened to their friend in 1971? Talk about a breach of trust.

I read the pages again, combing through each minor detail the author laid out. She didn't seem scared for her safety but she did appear to be very uncomfortable. These were boys whom she had grown up with, old friends and high school classmates and they didn't seem to care too much about her uneasiness.

"Piece of ass ..." Edward's description of my mother sliced through my thoughts. I knew using those words was Ed's way of dehumanizing my mom. She was never a whole person, she was just a body part, something someone could use without feeling guilty. Never mind that there was a living soul attached to that ass. Forget that she had raised his child without his help. Ignore the fact that her heart was bigger than anything else she had going for her.

"Richter," Amy said. "Why do I know that name? It sounds familiar." Amy brought up Facebook. We found Bruce and he appeared to still be friends with Edward, but then Amy said, "Bruce Richter is also friends with your Uncle Greg."

I frowned. My Uncle Greg is my dad's younger brother.

Amy looked harder. "Your Uncle Greg and Bruce Richter are brothers-in-law." Amy looked confused. "Bruce Richter is good friends with Edward. Bruce's son Jacob and Edward's youngest son Kevin also appear to be really good friends."

I blinked. This just hit close to home. "Well, shit."

* *
*

I did my best to place Edward on the back burner to simmer while I turned my attention to the one thing that all of us were looking forward to that summer: The Ward Family Reunion. Amy was in charge of the planning. It was held in her dad's hometown of Melrose, Iowa. It was a full weekend of boating, swimming, eating, street dances, games, laughing, and drinking. All five of us needed it—a weekend away with our big, loud, Irish family was the needed break from our thoughts about our big, loud, German family.

The first Friday of the reunion was boating day. An entire afternoon, divided on two pontoons on Lake Rathbun, the largest lake in Iowa. We boarded a boat with nine of Amy's relatives and took off. It was a picture-perfect day, not a cloud in the sky, the sun high above our heads. Everyone was relaxed and we enjoyed watching as our girls took turns water tubing off the back of the boat.

A couple of hours passed, and we idled the boat so Catey and Jillian could swim over to the ladder to reboard. Jillian made it to the ladder and climbed in, Catey was swimming over when a gentle wave pushed her away from the side of the boat and toward the back. In one second time, the propeller, still in an easy idle, twirled and snagged the mesh of her swimsuit. Catey was immediately sucked up against the propeller.

"Cut the engine!" I heard someone yell. I ran to the back and looked down. Catey was smashed into the propeller, just her face bobbing above the surface. The water lapped under her and I could see her swimsuit separate from her abdomen. Two red lines ran vertically on both sides of her torso, slashes from the propeller. Just then another wave rolled up and the back of the boat teetered. The propeller went under the water. Catey went under the water.

I jumped in.

The next few minutes were a mix of terror and chaos. I swam to Catey and wrapped one arm around her for support, while using my other arm to survey her tangled swimsuit. From above, Amy's cousins clustered around and one of them handed me a pocketknife. I started cutting the mesh pieces of Catey's swimsuit as we bobbed up and down together. A few seconds we would be above the water and then a few seconds we would be pulled under the water. As we surfaced, we could hear the terrified voices from above.

After what felt like a lifetime, Amy's cousin Pete reached down and grabbed Catey's arms to help keep her head above water. With his help, I was able to free her swimsuit and separated Catey from the propeller. Exhausted, we both boarded the boat. Amy's family wrapped us in towels and gave us water. Amy and I took turns holding Catey close. After a few breaths, Pete asked, "Ready to head back?"

"Yes!" everyone shouted.

That night, we tucked the girls in at the hotel, appreciative of the day, hopeful that the rest of the weekend would be less exciting than the first day. Amy and I lay down and as we all fell asleep, Catey said, "I can still feel the water."

"It's okay," Amy soothed. "You're in bed. You're safe now."

Catey was quiet. "I could have died today."

I swallowed. "But you didn't."

"But I could have."

"You didn't die because Dad loves you so much that he jumped in and saved you!" Jillian piped in.

Things were quiet. Then Catey said, "Thanks, Dad, you're a really good dad."

I frowned. "Just be quiet now, honey, and try to get some sleep."

I closed my eyes and fell into a restless sleep. I dreamed I was a little boy again, around three years old, and I was sitting at a dinner table. Everyone had finished eating and left the dirty dishes and food scraps behind. I was there, sitting on top of the table, among the piles of leftovers. A cleaning crew came along and started shoveling the food and plates into large garbage bags. I noticed another little boy sitting on the far side of the table. The crew threw him into the garbage sack, along with some half-eaten turkey. The closer they got to me, the more I noticed other little kids were being thrown away. Just as they were about to grab me, I felt a tug on my arm and my dad was there, dressed in his Army uniform. He was much younger, in his mid-twenties, around the time he had married my mom. He lifted me in his arms and told the cleaning crew, "Not this one. He belongs to me."

I awoke with a jolt, my arms suspended in the air. For a second I thought I saw someone looking down at me. I knew I was seeing my father. But I couldn't make out which one.

THIRTY-THREE

Summer was coming to an end. August arrived and, as I had felt in the past, I didn't want to call Edward. I wanted him to call me. I was privy to some information regarding his summer. From Google, I was able to see that his oldest son, Adam, had completed his tour of the county jails and was now in rehab. I was told that Edward's middle son, Mark, and his family had sold their house and accepted new jobs in Alabama. They had made the move down south a couple of weeks prior, in mid-July. Both events were big. I was certain Edward was preoccupied with the weight of his own family and those things would surely overshadow a phone conversation with me.

I could only assume that, unlike me, Edward had kept his end of the no-contact summer pact. I was certain he most likely had not talked to anyone about me, with the exception of Bev. I, however, had sent him Catey's letter, had emailed Louisa, and had talked on the phone with both Carolyn and Marty. Edward wasn't aware of any of that. The only information he would be able to gather about me or my family would be what Amy and I had posted on Facebook. He didn't know about the struggles I had all summer long. How every day that passed, I told myself if he really wanted to know me, he would know me. He wouldn't have needed a stupid break. If he really wanted to know me, he would grow some balls and stand up to his wife. He would tell her that he was going to take responsibility and proceed forward. He would do those things, if he really wanted to know me.

Louisa, Carolyn, and Marty had all told me that Edward was actually the reasonable one of the family.

"Even when he doesn't agree with the situation," Marty told me. "He listens to the other side and tries to understand where the person is coming from."

Except for me. I was the one situation where Edward couldn't get on the other side.

Sperm Donor. My mom had used that term. *We can just call him Ed, the sperm donor.* It wasn't the first time I had heard of my biological father being referred to this way. It wouldn't be the last. It was said like it was a joke. "Your father was a sperm donor." Like he wasn't real.

Edward didn't feel like a sperm donor, though. To me, he felt like a real living person. A guy who looked like me, moved like me, and laughed like me. I wasn't conceived in a cold, mechanical clinical setting with doctors and nurses and rubber gloves. I was conceived...

My mind buckled at the thought, an immediate mental roadblock bricked together, blocking me from thinking any further. Amy was the youngest of six. Her parents celebrated nineteen years of marriage the year she was born. The friends I grew up with were born from parents who loved each other. Our kids were born out of the love Amy and I shared. My sisters were born from my parents' love. Edward and Bev's boys were born out of their love.

I was not conceived out of love. I was born from a mistake. A reckless decision that my teenage mother and father made. I was such a bad choice that one of them decided to bail. And now here I was, phone in hand, sending a Hail Mary up—just in case there was someone up there—that this phone call wouldn't be our last. I knew if I didn't make the call, he never would.

I scrolled down to Edward's name, pushed send, and pressed the phone to my ear. He answered on the second ring.

I wish I could remember everything that was said. I didn't write this conversation down. Edward was cold and distant and from the moment he answered, he was desperate to get off the call.

"This is as far as this is going to go," he told me.

"Okay, so . . . there is no change with —"

"No."

"Bev just couldn't —"

"No."

"All right." I swallowed. "Um, I do need you to know a couple of things. The first is some of your family reached out to me —"

"My family?"

"Yeah, a couple of your siblings—"

"My siblings? Who? Which ones?"

I paused. To tell or not to tell? At this point I knew what side my heart was on. "I'm not going to name any names. I don't know if they are ready for you to know that they are speaking to me."

"Fine. Don't tell me." Fighting words. Like we were teenage brothers, not estranged father and son.

"If you're curious which of them are speaking to me, you can always call them up and ask them yourself."

"That won't be happening."

Edward had been living in the dark for forty-five years about me. If he wanted to continue living that way, there wasn't anything more I could do to enlighten him.

"Okay." I shrugged. "The second thing is I have continued to match with other relatives on Ancestry and a few of them have messaged me. A couple of your cousins—"

"I don't care about any of them."

I ignored him. "Some of the last names of these people are Blaschke, Harrison, Leonard, Rincon –"

"I don't care."

"And Horner."

"Horner?" He was surprised. "What's the first name?"

"I don't remember," I replied. "I would have to look it up."

He was quiet and then resolved, "I don't care about any of them."

"You don't?"

"No, I don't speak to any of those people."

I nodded. "Okay then, I want you to know that if any Schneyder relative reaches out to me from this point on, I'm going to reach back. I am not turning anyone away."

Edward sighed. "That is not what we want to hear."

We. He hadn't mentioned her name once, but there it was: *we.* "Well, that's what I'm telling you."

I could feel the heat on the other side of the line. "It's not going to go any further than this. I accept that I'm your father and if someone asks me, I will not deny who you are. But we are not going to talk openly about this, and we are *never* going to tell our boys."

"That may be a problem because letting my half-brothers know about me is my end game," I said.

"Not gonna happen."

"If that's how you want to play it, that's your choice."

"*I* can't tell our boys about you," Edward said.

Not *we* this time. He emphasized "I." Edward and I sat, stewing in our own feelings, waiting for the other person to speak. I caved. "If you can't tell them, I can."

"You're gonna do what you're gonna do."

What the hell did that mean? "I'm just trying to give you a heads up."

"Bev won't let me tell our boys. You do whatever you want."

There was my permission, not that I needed it. "If you need to get in touch with me," I started—

"I got your number right here in my phone."

"And I got yours."

Again, silence.

"Thanks," I said. "For coming as far as you did. I really do appreciate it and..." I hesitated. I didn't want this to end. I wanted to tell him that. I wanted to tell him I was sorry for all the disruption I caused. I wanted to tell him that I wanted him in my life. I swallowed hard, pushing down all the years robbed from me. "My door is always open to you," I said. "It will never close."

A pause. For a second I thought he had already hung up. Then, a shaky voice: "Okay. Good-bye."

"Bye."

THIRTY-FOUR

Ever since I was a young boy I have wanted a brother. I loved my sisters but as is human nature, I often found myself desiring things I didn't have. And, on my short list of big, bulging biceps, the ability to grow a mustache, to own a brand new Mustang, I also wanted a brother.

Side note: as I grew older, I achieved the mustache!

The rest, not so much.

I have done a lot of research reading about struggles from other adoptees and NPEs (Not Parent Expected—people mostly like me, who discovered at some point in their life that one or both parents was in fact not biological). I have had the opportunity to talk to others who have stories similar to mine. In the not knowing periods of their lives, almost every single one speculates about brothers and sisters. Some of them are more curious to know about siblings than they are their own parents. It's a marvelous thing having another person by your side who is ready to face the world with you. Through laughter and tears, fists and hugs, that person has your back. Siblings = friends. Whether you love them or hate them, it's hard to imagine life without them. I knew what that was like with sisters. I wondered what it would be like with a brother.

Of course, as with finding a birth parent, adoptees tend to romanticize about newfound siblings as well. And I fell right into that trap.

From speaking to my two aunts and now my new Uncle Marty,

one common thread that they all spoke about was their belief that if my brothers knew about me, they would be welcoming.

"They will want to know you," Carolyn insisted. "I know it. They are good boys."

"The youngest is probably your best bet to start with," Louisa told me. "The oldest is in rehab, he may need to be shielded from all of this right now. The middle son is very close to Bev. He may be able to help her through her feelings."

"I'm close with all of them—well, two of them," Marty told me. I knew, without him telling me, that the one he was omitting was Adam. "They're cool guys but they have a lot going on in their lives right now. I'm sure they will want to get to know you. I just...I don't want to be the one to tell them about you. Ed should do it. Or, you could."

He was right. I could tell them. Edward and Bev weren't going to do it and I didn't want to put that kind of responsibility on any of my aunts or uncles. The news that I existed was still being whispered about through the family and spreading across the town. I was fearful that one of my brothers would find out from an outside source. That wasn't fair to anyone. Even though I didn't know them personally, I genuinely cared about them. If just one of them wanted to know me, that would be a win in my book. And maybe if they handled the news well, it would erase some of the fear within Bev. If she could see with her own eyes that her sons knew about me and they were okay with it, maybe that would release some of her anxiety and she could find a way forward with Edward, with their boys, with me, with my family.

I decided to write them a letter. I had been fortunate that Edward had responded to the letter I wrote him, maybe I could get lucky again. I sent the letter through Facebook as a private message but it never looked like they were viewed and so I also sent them a hard copy through the mail. I only wrote the middle and youngest sons, Mark and Kevin. I chose to exclude Adam, on purpose, as I didn't want to be a trigger for any future success in rehab.

I hoped my letter would be welcomed warmly. I really, really hoped.

SUNDAY, AUGUST 13, 2017

Dear Mark/Kevin,

Hello, my name is Michael Blair. Earlier this year, I took an Ancestry DNA test and upon getting my results, I was matched to a biological aunt, Louisa Schmidt and a second cousin, Jerry Wachtel. After doing some investigating (with help from Louisa), I was able to narrow down whom I thought was my biological father.

In February, I contacted Edward Schneyder, and he immediately responded and met me at a DNA lab in Des Moines. The results were conclusive that we are father and son, 99.99% match.

You—Kevin, Mark and Adam—are my biological half-brothers.

My journey with your father, has been fascinating. I have learned more about myself and where I originated from than I ever dreamed I would know. Edward and I have had a handful of phone conversations and we have met twice over the past six months. It has been quite a shock and a disruption for Edward and Bev. They are having difficulty accepting this news.

A little bit about myself: I was raised by my biological mother and adopted father and grew up in the Des Moines and Altoona area. My relationship with my parents has been problematic in the past because I never knew who my father was.

After many conversations with my parents, we are in a good place today. My wife Amy and I have been married for nearly 24 years. We have three girls: Roslyn(19), Catherine (14), and Jillian (12). We live in Johnston, Iowa. After several years of working as a graphic designer,

I switched gears and became a professor of design at Des Moines Area Community College in Ankeny. I've enjoyed teaching full-time since 2007. Hobbies include: traveling, photography, going to concerts, hanging with friends and enjoying a good cocktail.

I understand receiving a message like this is surprising. Because of this, I am writing just the two of you. I am aware that Adam has had some problems in the past and currently is going through a life change of his own. This may not be the time for him to know about me and I want to handle that with the utmost care.

My goal is to meet all three of my half-brothers one day, but I want it to be at a time when each of you is ready to meet me, if you choose. I am not reaching out to you to cause a disruption or cause problems, I'm reaching out to let you know that I am here and I am open to a friendship with any of you.

If you're interested, please feel free to contact me and we can make arrangements to talk and/or meet in the future. My Facebook profile is public, feel free to stalk me. I also sent you this letter via Facebook Messenger, but it didn't look like it was received.

Hope to hear from you soon,

    Michael Blair

I took a breath. Then, I wrote a letter to Edward.

SUNDAY, AUGUST 13, 2017

Dear Edward,

Thank you for being as open as you can to me this year. I know it's been a shock to you and Bev. I'm very grateful that I was able to talk and meet with you this past six months. It's been quite the adventure and I understand where you stand in this situation.

Although I understand, I still need to continue on my journey. The *people who have reached out to me will be reciprocated. I have nothing but open arms, heart and mind to the Schneyder families. Any relationships I gain, no matter how small, will be an incredible bonus to me and my family.*

The greatest thing to come of this adventure is that I have been able to repair damaged relationships with my parents. They are amazing people for being supportive of all of this. Especially with my mom. We've had some long overdue talks this summer. She faced many challenges raising me. She has also let me in on her side of the story of how you and she met. While it is completely different from your story, I've let it go. It doesn't matter. Regardless of what the truth is, I'm very lucky to be alive and have the life that I have. I'm proud to be half of both of you.

I wish you the best of luck and hope to meet with you again some day.
With Respect,
Michael Blair

THIRTY-FIVE

The rest of August was greeted with complete silence.

I checked my Facebook twice a day and every evening I came home with a question on my face.

"You didn't get anything in the mail," was the response.

I was haunted by the chaos that must be happening in Lawrence. What had I done? What turmoil had I caused? It couldn't be good because no one was calling me, telling me that they were thrilled to hear they had another brother and wanted to meet for a beer.

"Good things come to those who wait," Amy said. Like she was being helpful. I resisted the urge to yell at her.

The waiting was unbearable. The silence was deafening.

Every Sunday I walked next door to my neighbor's basement where I spent an hour with the other guys in the hood, watching *Game of Thrones*. Season Seven Awesomeness.

"*I drink and I know things.*"—*Tyrion Lannister.* I mean, come on—who comes up with this shit? It's phenomenal writing, that's what that is.

Sitting among my friends, discussing who was going to actually win the throne, the discussion heated up. "Tyrion deserves the throne!" "Cersei won't get it!" "And don't forget the bastard!"

Ah, yes, the bastard. Every goddamn show. In *Game of Thrones*, this would be Jon Snow. Most everyone who watched the show could agree on two things—they loved Tyrion and Jon Snow. The whole allure of Jon Snow is his dark past—was he the illegitimate son of Ned Stark or, as it's discovered in Season Seven—is his father someone else? On top of his heavy fur coat of many animal pelts, Jon Snow is also weighted down with the burden of the question mark.

I sat with my neighbors and watched the show, but my mind wandered to the unanswered letters. I felt the pain of my brothers' silence was burning away any DNA connection we had. Disassociating and severing. Just as Jon Snow's half-siblings had made it very clear to him: You are not worthy to be part of this family. You are not a full breed. You are only half.

SEPTEMBER 2017

Amy and I and the girls all tried to stay positive. September was the month of Schneyder, as we affectionately called it. First, we met with Jerry Wachtel, my second cousin match on Ancestry. He was the first biological relative that we all got to touch. We met at a local Maid Rite and had an easy conversation with him and his wife Janet. They were both open and warm. He was a great historian on the Harrisons, which was my Grandmother Schneyder's side of the family. He conversed about memories of going to my grandparents' house when he was young and playing with his cousins.

"They were . . . poor." Jerry nodded. "I mean, my family had seven kids and we didn't have any money but when we went over to play with Uncle George and Aunt Pauline's family, it was like they were living the way people would have lived fifty years in the past. They had all those kids and used well water and there were animals to milk and I think there was an outhouse. I remember when I looked around at their house, it was different than mine. Like I said, they were poor."

"So, they were hard workers," I said, trying to find a positive spin.

"Very," Jerry agreed. "They worked hard." He paused. "And, really, when you look at them today, they have all done fairly well for themselves."

"Sounds like their parents must have done something right, then."

Jerry picked at his Maid Rite. "Edward has not spoken to me since he found out that I know about you. He's pretty much cut me off. Not that we were particularly close," Jerry pointed out.

The words *cut off* resonated with me. "I'm sorry,"I softly said.

Jerry waved a dismissive hand. "Don't be. I'm not."

I asked if we could take some pictures, strictly for my own use. "I won't post them on Facebook or anything," I assured him.

"Please do—I don't care if they are out there," he told me as he threw an arm over my shoulder and smiled. *Click.* We spent an hour and a half with the Wachtels and then they continued on their way. I decided to be bold and post the photos of me and Jerry. Here was my first bio-relative, one who was comfortable with my transparency, who accepted me as family, and he didn't care who saw it.

And neither did I. Under the posted picture I wrote: *I met my second cousin Jerry Wachtel from Texas yesterday, when he rolled through Iowa. We're no longer perfect strangers.*

Next, we met Louisa and her husband Jay. They were in Iowa to celebrate the 101st birthday of one of her aunts. Personally, my mother's relatives pretty much all died before they turned seventy but over here, this family had an aunt who was more than one hundred years old—and still living by herself in her house! My newly discovered grandparents had lived to be eighty-nine and ninety-one. These genes came with longevity.

We met Louisa and Henry on a late Sunday morning at Centro, a downtown Des Moines eatery. Like any local restaurant on a Sunday, brunch was popular, but when we walked in, it was like we owned the place. We were seated at a large table in the middle of the room, there were only a few customers around us, and we scored on the waiter. He was attentive and charming.

We were positioned so we could see the door. I chose to sit away from it so I wouldn't be tempted to look every time someone walked in, but I could see Amy checking it, which was almost worse. Louisa and Henry were late, so I was nervous for an extra twenty minutes. What if they forgot? What if they had an accident? What if they got lost? And, worst of all, what if they changed their minds?

My leg was shaking so badly, the entire table shook along with it.

"There they are," Amy said as she stood up. The girls stood up. I stood up. I turned around and there she was—this petite, white haired lady with my eyes—she had my eyes—and a big, bright smile, walking my way. All her attention was on me. I felt like she was soaking me in. She held recognition and acceptance in one incredible smile.

"Michael," she said, and her arms wrapped around me.

Unknown to me, I had been carrying around a broken heart. I realized it in this moment because in one move, Louisa mended part of it, a stitch repaired.

Amy and the girls greeted Henry and then we switched, we made surface introductions, and sat down. Louisa was seated next to me. Henry sat at the head of the table. He was a smaller man, comparable to Louisa in height. He was graying and had that kind of look where you just sensed he was a calming presence in this world. Henry's sense of humor was sharp—but he wasn't overbearing, he had comedic timing and was smart with his comments.

I instantly liked both of them.

We ordered food and drinks and talked about their trip down from the Lawrence area. They were staying with Louisa's sister, Mary, who knew about me, but hadn't shown any interest in meeting me.

"Does she know you're here?" Amy asked.

"She does."

"What does she say about that?"

Louisa hesitated. "We don't talk about it. Besides mentioning that Henry and I were coming here today, we have not spoken about any of this." She waved a hand around the table.

I was surprised. The way these people dealt with a crisis amazed me. Amy was the youngest of six and if either of her brothers had fathered a child none of them had ever known about, it would be discussed on a regular basis. Her family would help her brother accept his child. They would never be stuck in limbo, as this family seemed to be.

"Besides the ones that you conversed with in the beginning, have any of your other siblings been told about us?" Amy pressed.

"Not that I am aware of." Louisa paused. "I don't bring it up to any of them."

I frowned. "Why?"

"Because," she looked at me, "it's not my story to tell."

I nodded. I had a love/hate relationship with that phrase. I understood the importance of it, giving ownership to those who the story belonged to but I also wrestled with the other side. When I asked my own grandparents and my aunts and uncles, "Why didn't you ever tell me that Dad wasn't my biological dad?" They responded exactly like Louisa, "Because it wasn't my story to tell. Your mother needed to tell you."

But what happens if that person doesn't tell? Are all of those who are witnesses to the secret supposed to remain quiet? Are they supposed to stand by and watch as a person continues to be lied to? When does responsibility shift to those who know but won't tell?

Time is the enemy of secret keepers. Eventually, a secret does what it was always intended to do: it explodes.

"You are the first biological great aunt that we have ever met on my Dad's side," Rosie said.

That was true. My Aunt Linda had died when Rosie was three months old. On my adopted dad's side, the girls had only met my aunt and uncles once, when they were very young. Catey and Jillian had no recollection of it.

Much of our conversation revolved around the DNA results and how it had impacted Louisa's life thus far. She and Henry were former educators and counselors and so they were able to take this news in stride. They had a unique way of looking at it, choosing to take a positive stand, instead of negative. "When I first got the news, my initial reaction was—this is exciting! It was a mystery to solve. And then, as you know, as Edward's reaction turned out to not be ideal, my eagerness was kind of pushed to the side. Of course, your impact to Henry and me hasn't been as great as it has been to Edward. Finding a nephew versus finding a child are two very different things."

I got that. It seemed the family who no longer lived in the Lawrence area were much more receptive to me than family who resided in close proximity to Edward. That made sense. Distance already separated the family, whether they acknowledged it or not, so it was easier to deal with Edward's disapproval when you didn't have to run into him at the local Dollar Store.

Henry took a drink. "We're still excited about you, though. All of you."

"Yes," Louisa easily agreed. "We are."

We left Centro and Louisa and Henry met us at our house for dessert. We sat at our dining room table and conversed some more. They told us then that not only were they back to see Louisa's aunt but also to attend a surprise birthday party for one of Louisa's brothers-in-law. The party had been the night before and they had spent quality time with both Edward and Bev, along with my two half-brothers, Mark and Kevin, and their wives.

"Oh." I breathed. "How was that?"

"They were very relaxed," Louisa said, her eyebrows arching, a motion I recognized as something mine also did. "Of course, you were not discussed but it was a very easy conversation. They are all adjusting to their new lives, living apart from one another. Mark and his wife Jenny are getting used to living in Alabama." She paused. "Have you heard from either of the boys?"

I shook my head. The longer I waited, the more hope I lost that I ever would hear from them. It was like I mailed my letters to Siberia and they would just keep traveling on, never reaching their destination. "Bev must have them all by their balls," I said.

Louisa grimaced. "Bev is really a wonderful lady. When I think of some of the silly things she has gotten herself into . . ." Louisa laughed and exchanged a look with Henry. Her laughter quieted as she seemed to remember that we didn't share any of those memories. "I'm sure the boys feel an obligation to her," she said, subdued.

"I know they do," I agreed. And I did. I also thought they were a bunch of pussies but I didn't want to blurt that out. Instead, I went with, "But they're also adults. I would hope they would have the ability to think for themselves. If I found out that I had a brother who I never knew existed and he reached out to me, I would reach back. I would never leave a person hanging in limbo like this. Even if my mommy told me not to." My words held a bite of hostility that I couldn't hide. Louisa picked right up on it.

"Originally when you contacted me and I spoke with Edward, I really did think this was going to end well for both of you. To my fault, I tried very hard to be protective of both you and Edward. I understood this was a sensitive topic but it was one that I was hopeful would result in a relationship. Bev's reaction is not your fault. I have personally been surprised at her response to this. I didn't think she would take it so hard."

"We understand that Bev didn't ask for any of this," Amy said. "For better, For worse. This is worse. When she agreed to marry Edward forty years ago, she didn't ask for Michael to come along and turn her happy family upside down." Amy paused. "And the boys didn't ask for this either."

I nodded. "We are sympathetic," I knew that had to sound like a bunch of bullshit to Louisa's ears, but it was the truth. There wasn't a move that we made where we didn't ask ourselves how we would feel in the situation. Amy and I discussed it at length. So far, our own presumed reactions were the exact opposite of how Edward and Bev actually reacted. "I know they didn't ask for this, but I didn't ask to be born. I didn't ask to be conceived the way I was. I didn't ask for my father to run out on my mom and I didn't ask for him to keep me a secret." *I'm the victim in this situation,* Edward's voice echoed in my head.

Louisa was kind. From her earlier conversations with Edward and from his initial response to finding out about me, her theory was he probably did know my mom was pregnant with me. "He was young," she said. "He was only nineteen and nineteen-year-old boys do stupid things."

"Yeah," I replied, half-heartedly. I had been nineteen once, too. I would have never left a seventeen-year-old girl who was pregnant with my baby to fend for herself, but I understood many nineteen-year-old boys were selfish.

"I really think with a little more time, he is going to come around and then the boys will follow."

I smiled. I really wanted Louisa to be right. I wanted to believe. Edward had said to me once, *"You have known that I have been out here for twenty-five years and I just found out about you on Tuesday. I need some time."*

I could wait, even though I was convinced that Edward knew since day one. But, I could pretend that he just found out. I could wait. What other choice did I have?

* * *

One week later all five of us made the trip up to Salem, Iowa, just outside of Lawrence, to meet Aunt Carolyn and her husband, Randy. They lived in an old, beautiful farmhouse on acres of land, right off a gravel road. It was picture-perfect rural Iowa. A happy, pudgy chocolate lab came running up to greet us. When she wagged her tail, her entire back half wagged with her.

Meeting Carolyn and Randy was much different than meeting Aunt Louisa and Cousin Jerry. We were on their turf, in their home, and we were their guests. Carolyn made a delicious lasagna. Randy and I shared beers together. Carolyn doted on the girls and she engaged Amy in conversation. They were fantastic hosts.

At one point, we went into their living room where we sat around on the floor. Carolyn had numerous family photo albums stacked and we all took one and flipped through them. Carolyn walked around, swapping stories and giving her take about different family members. She used a lot of positive words to describe them: "Funny, smart, a saint, loving, life of the party, jolly . . ." She rarely spoke a negative word.

The only time she said anything where Edward fell into some bad light was when Carolyn admitted, "In the beginning, when I heard the news about you, Ed called me. I was at a doctor's appointment so he left me a voicemail where he advised me that I was not to talk about you and that if I had already, I was to cease and desist. He said what I heard wasn't true and that he was handling the situation." Carolyn shrugged. "I didn't call him back but I knew he was just covering his tracks. I had already seen pictures of you and you look just like him."

I thought about Edward's last phone call with me. *I will not deny who you are.* A cease and desist threat seemed to be a bit over the top, but Carolyn had mentioned it was said in the beginning of my discovery. Still, I couldn't imagine ever saying such things to one of my sisters. I loved them too much.

"I have some gifts," Carolyn announced.

We had brought gifts, too. Our motto was: "If they meet us, we bring a gift." We brought out our presents and exchanged them with Randy and Carolyn. Mine were socks and a silver dollar. Carolyn teared up as she explained how when they were young, her grandma would buy all the grandsons socks, while her grandpa would give them all a silver dollar.

Side note: Three years later, those socks are still being worn! Magic socks!

Amy opened her gift and received three baby blankets, which my Grandmother Schneyder had quilted. The girls opened their presents and inside were doilies. We found out that my Great-Grandmother Schneyder made them and would give them to all her granddaughters and great-granddaughters.

So much history in one night. So many precious keepsakes.

"We're all in with you guys," Carolyn said. She turned to her husband Randy. "I should say that I am all in. You're my nephew and I'm your Aunt Carolyn."

Randy looked up at us. "I'm in, too," he said. "I admit when I first heard about you, I was nervous. I didn't think we should get involved. I didn't want to step on Ed's toes so I thought we should wait this out and see what move he made first." Randy let out a breath. "The longer I thought about it, the more I put myself in Ed's shoes and came to realize that there was a right way and a wrong way to handle things. I want to be in the right, even if Ed isn't. I could never deny myself my own child and I would hope that my wife wouldn't deny me my child, either. So, as your uncle," he waved his hand in a circle, "you are welcomed here. You and your entire family."

Carolyn started crying. My girls were crying. Amy had teared up. I walked over and hugged my aunt. And, just as with hugging Louisa, my new Aunt Carolyn mended a portion of my heart that I never realized had been torn.

"I've also thought about what I think Ed would do if he were in your position," Randy continued. "Ed and I have been good friends over the years, and I know him pretty well. I truly believe if Ed was in the same situation that you are in and he found out that he had a different biological father, I think Ed would do the exact same thing that you have. He would drop everything and immerse himself in research until he found out that man's identity and he would find where he was and if he had siblings and if he did, he would reach out to them. In fact, I think Ed would be much more aggressive than you have been."

I gave an appreciative smile. "Thanks for that," I said. It was comforting to know that someone who knew Edward felt that I was doing what he would do, if the circumstances were reversed. Randy's words rang true to my grandparents' story that my biological father showed up on their doorstep. What was more aggressive than walking up to a stranger's door, knocking, and asking the people who lived there if a girl you had slept with five years before had ever had her baby?

That kind of guts took some pretty big balls. That kind of guts was probably an inherited trait.

"Ed is a fun-loving guy," Randy said.

I nodded. "I'm sure he is a barrel of laughs."

"But he can be a real asshole, too." Randy smiled.

My girls and Amy pointed at me. "Yes!" they shouted.

Apparently, the apple didn't fall far from the tree.

THIRTY-SIX

Meeting Louisa and Carolyn had been invigorating.

Both women were fundamentally different in the way they chose to live their lives, although after spending time with them, I was able to spot similarities in their mannerisms and the way they behaved. They were sisters, raised under the same roof, albeit almost ten years apart from each other. Nonetheless they were family, rooted from the same stock and from there, expanding out to create their own family branches.

One thing they agreed on was they had room for me on their limbs. Louisa and Carolyn embraced my girls, and they were lovely to Amy. In a time when I was being rejected by my bio-father and greeted with silence from my bio-brothers, these women held space for me in their own families.

I still had to meet Marty.

Amy and I had close friends whose son played for the Cyclones, so I was somewhat familiar with the football schedule and Jack Trice Stadium. I had been eagerly watching the Thursday night, September 28 game get closer on my calendar.

Marty had shot me a message requesting a meeting with me the Wednesday evening before the game. I accepted his invitation. Both Louisa and Carolyn were surprised to hear that Marty agreed to meet with me but, like me, they were hopeful that perhaps his involvement would be the key needed to change Edward's mind on ending our contact. Marty, however, seemed to have a hard time understanding that Edward was done speaking to me. Marty texted frequently.

Marty: *Did you send the letters to the boys?*

Me: *Yes, but just Mark and Kevin. Not Adam.*

Marty: *Good thinking. Have you heard anything from them yet?*

Me: *Not a peep.*

This went on for about two weeks prior to us meeting.

Marty: *I want you to know that I think what you are doing is very brave. My brother is the kind of person who will need to take time with this. I have hope that you two will be able to have a wonderful relationship. You may have lost years, but my wish is for you and Ed to enjoy the next thirty ahead of you.*

I laughed. Like Edward would be alive for thirty more years. Hell, like I would be alive for thirty more years. I texted back.

Me: *Yeah, that would be something.*

A few days would go by and then my phone would ping.

Marty: *Have you heard from Ed lately?*

Me: *Not since August 5, when he told me we wouldn't be talking anymore.*

Marty: *He said that?*

Me: *Yes.*

I had already discussed this with Marty. I could sense it bothered him that Edward was no longer speaking to me, that neither Mark nor Kevin had contacted me, and that Marty had this pressing date with me coming up.

Marty: *Maybe I should talk to Mark for you?*

Now, I have to admit, I wanted this. I wanted somebody in the Schneyder family to talk to someone in Edward's family and tell them that they were in contact with me. I thought if Edward and Bev knew that one of their family members was speaking to me—and that person still loved them and wanted to continue their relationship with them exactly as it was—that this would be a positive move. Edward would see that his brother was able to get to know me, form a friendship with me, and continue his own solid relationship with Edward. It didn't have to be either/or. It could be both. It was possible to be on speaking terms with me and still love and respect Edward. Maybe if someone could step up and do that, the fear that Edward and Bev held about my existence would start to dissipate. They could see that it was okay. I wasn't that scary. That no one thought less of them. No one blamed them for anything.

Me: *If you're comfortable doing that, I'm fine with it.*

Marty: *Let me think about it for a couple of days.*

That exchange occurred on September 14. We were to meet two weeks later.

SEPTEMBER 19, 2017

Marty texted.

Michael,

I will not be meeting with you on Wednesday. I have done some investigating and have discovered that you have misled me and have been untruthful about how your mother and my brother met and the circumstances that led to you being born. You have been very aggressive and disrespectful when dealing with my brother. You have been deceitful towards my nephews. You did not listen to me when I told you to give my brother time and space. I know Edward better than any of my other siblings. You didn't follow anything that I told you to do. Your only choice is to step back if you want any kind of future with my brother.

I will not jeopardize the position I hold with my brother. He means more to me than you. I cannot believe that you met with Jerry Wachtel! My family does not respect him! I told you not to talk to him! And why would you ever want to meet with Louisa? You have nothing to gain in meeting her!

Because of my loyalty to my brother, I will not be meeting you or talking to you again. Not until my brother is okay with it. I doubt he will ever accept you after everything you have done! You are tearing my family apart!

I threw my phone at Amy and let her read it. I considered reading it out loud but I knew that if I did, I would break down. That's what I was doing, wasn't it? Breaking down?

Amy looked up. "Your only choice is to step back if you want any kind of future with my brother," she read. "Wow, it's a rave review! It's way better than we thought—there's still hope!" She said sarcastically. "He didn't mention Carolyn, just Louisa and Jerry so...he must not know we've met Carolyn. He knows we met with Jerry because you posted the pictures on Facebook. He's talked to somebody in the family—Edward or Mark—and they must have told him that we met Louisa." She handed my phone back to me. "You're going to have to respond."

The words were still fresh, still running through my head. *Liar. Untruthful. Nothing to gain. Aggressive. Didn't listen to me. Tearing my family apart.* I thought about taking a day or two to sleep on it, weave my words more eloquently, yet if I waited too long I would most likely overthink things and I wouldn't respond at all. If I were going to reply, I needed to do it now.

Hi, Marty—I'm sorry if you feel that I have not followed a proper route in dealing with your family. This has not been an easy journey for me. In fact, it is the hardest thing I have ever done in my life. I have attempted to maintain as much transparency as I can and I am sure that there have been missteps in my handling of things.

I am only human, I am sure I have made mistakes moving forward with Edward. As far as speaking and meeting with members of your family, I am not a mind reader. I do not know what problems you or Edward have had in the past with your relatives and, honestly, I don't care. Your issues with them are not my problem. As far as I am concerned, I have a clean slate with everyone in the Schneyder family.

My family and I met Jerry because he was my DNA connection on Ancestry and he was helpful in contacting Louisa. He invited me and my family to have lunch with him and his wife. I bought them a Maidrite and enjoyed an hour and a half of conversing with him. So far, I have spent more time talking and being accepted by Jerry Wachtel than I have my own biological father.

As for Louisa, the reason I met her is because she is my biological aunt. She is also an adult and has the ability to make her own decisions. What I have to gain with her is one more person in my life to love. You were willing to meet me prior to today, just as she was willing. The difference is she actually went through with it. You told me yourself that I could trust Louisa and could confide in her and now you are suddenly upset with me because we met.

I hope that you will reconsider meeting with me next week. I am still open to it and my wish is nothing more than to move forward and to ultimately have a friendship with you, Edward, my half-brothers, and, yes, Bev. I am unsure what you are talking about when you state that I was deceitful to your nephews. The only thing I have done is send Mark and Kevin a letter. I can forward it to you if you would like to read it. When deciding whether or not to send them a letter, I asked myself if I had a half-sibling out there in this world, would I want to know about him? I knew that answer was yes and so I decided to proceed in telling them. Maybe Edward's family is too fractured and in a place where they are not okay to accept this kind of news.

I hope to hear from you soon,

Michael

Later that evening, I discovered how Marty knew we met with Louisa when I received an email from Louisa, telling me that she, too, had decided to go forth and tell Edward she had met me and my family earlier in the month.

...I told Ed that Henry and I drove to Des Moines and had lunch with you and we found you and your family to be warm and loving. I told him if you were mine, I would be proud to tell people that you were my son.

I smiled. Louisa rocked! Then, she said he responded back.

Edward is furious with me for meeting with you. He has informed me that I am disowned and I will no longer be considered to be a part of their family going forward.

I was sick. I emailed her back, telling her about my response from Marty.

I'm troubled that I may have caused damage within the family. This is heartbreaking. I don't think people understand that I have been shooting blind. Yes, I was cautioned against building relations with some people but, there are a lot of you and I cannot change your past experiences with one another. To me, family is family. I have tried to place all of you on an equal playing ground ...

...I don't know what the best course of action should be from here. I know that it upsets Edward to know that I'm talking to anyone from the family; however, I don't want to throw away the relationships I have built. I'm torn. I know that I don't have to live in Edward's denial but, at the same time, I don't want to be the reason anyone fights and I certainly don't want to be the reason why a family divides even more. Should I stay or should I go?

That was the question, wasn't it? To stay or not to stay. If I was going to bail, this was the time to do it, before we got any more attached because Louisa and Carolyn were wonderful, as were their husbands. I could only assume that in a family this large, there would be more great people who would want to know me and whom

I would fall in love with as I had with Louisa and Carolyn.

The week prior, I had felt so full... now, I was empty.

"I already love Louisa and Carolyn," I told Amy. I truthfully did. In the small amount of time I spent with them, I had been transported back in time to when I was a kid and would spend time with my Aunt Susan. That feeling that I was hers. The way she made me feel special when I was with her, when she looked at me and I saw recognition staring back. I felt the same way with Louisa and Carolyn. Deep down inside there was no denying it—these people were my family.

I closed my eyes and remembered Carolyn's words earlier the prior week, *"I'm all in. You're my nephew and I'm your Aunt Carolyn."* It amazed me how I clung to the words spoken by these people. At any moment, I thought, they are going to ditch me. The fear of being rejected was palpable and constantly in the back of my mind.

I was trouble. I wasn't worth all of the shit I was causing.

Louisa wrote back.

... I think that some family members (who are aware of the situation) are probably, like Marty, waiting to see how Edward, Bev and the boys handle it. For our part, Henry and I are delighted to know you and your family. We intend to pursue our relationship with you and your family regardless of how the rest of the family responds. We feel that our lives are richer for knowing you all. We encourage you to stay in contact and we look forward to getting to know each other better. I wish that we were geographically closer so that family BBQs and gatherings were easier to arrange! I give myself a daily pep talk: I will not take on Edward's anger; I am not angry. I have choices; I am an adult who makes the best choices that I can. I'm happy with my decisions; I would do it again.

Affectionately,

Louisa

THIRTY-SEVEN

I love a Sunday morning. Sleeping in, but still managing to be up before anyone else. I woke up that morning early and wandered downstairs to make myself an eggy in a basket. I turned on the TV and cracked an egg in a bowl. A commercial for the Cyclones popped on, singing the tag line, "Are you ready for some Thursday night football?"

I took a bite of my breakfast and immediately, my stomach turned.

I had been on the fence for a few days but, in that moment, I decided I couldn't let it pass without trying to reach out one more time to Marty. He was my biological uncle. He was going to the Cyclone game and would be thirty minutes away from me. I had to try. I texted him.

Hi, Marty -

I wanted to reach out to you once more. You made your intentions very clear in your previous text and I certainly understand not wanting to upset Edward by meeting me. I wish things were better between him and me and that more of the Schneyder Family felt comfortable in meeting me.

From the time I have been 18, I have fought for information regarding my biological father. I have fought my parents, lawyers, the courts, judges, and now that I have my basic answers, I feel like I'm still fighting to learn more about myself.

I may have made mistakes on this journey. There is no rule book for finding your bio-family and while there are those who may think I was too aggressive, some of it was not in my power. I have matched with many people on Ancestry and they have figured out who I am. It's been a difficult thing to control who finds out and when. I've explained this to Edward but he has never seemed to understand or care. Those who have reached out to me that I have talked to—Jerry and Louisa—have been extremely helpful and kind to me. So, yes, I met with them when they were back in Iowa for family functions.

Meeting Louisa was fantastic for me. I have no biological aunts or uncles and I thought she was wonderful. I feel badly about the way things have turned out with Edward. I have been more than open with him about my life. The choice to end any future for a friendship was his, not mine. I did not meet with Jerry or Louisa nor did I contact Mark or Kevin until after Edward told me he would not move forward and I told him what my intentions were.

Reaching out to your family is not an easy task. Every move I've made has been carefully thought through and required some bravery. This week, I know you're in town and I would like to meet you. If you would reconsider, that would be great. I will be in Ames at The Boulder Tap House on Wednesday evening. I will be there from 6pm to 8pm. If you would like to sit down and have a beer, the seat across from me will be open.

Michael Blair

I didn't receive any kind of acknowledgment in return but three days later, on that Wednesday, I packed my bag, locked my office, and took off from work. It was a straight shot up I-35. Twenty-five minutes later, I walked into The Boulder Tap, selected a table with two chairs, I ordered a beer, and pulled out my phone. I quietly began surfing the Internet, all the while studying the parking lot, casually watching cars pull in and out.

Thirty minutes went by. I answered a couple of emails. Another thirty minutes and I had played all my hands in Words with Friends. Two hours passed. I finished my third beer and pretzel sticks and clicked on Facebook. I typed in Marty's name.

Normally, his profile was locked down, but on this evening, I could see that he had entered a "check-in." It was from two hours before, at a Starbucks, across the street from my work.

I couldn't believe my eyes. "Son of a bitch." I had just been there—two hours before—packing up my shit. So, while I was driving north, thirty miles to meet him, Marty had driven the thirty miles beyond his destination, to set up shop, right across the street from where I had just left. Here I sat, like a sucker, waiting on him, while he taunted me.

I thought I was going to lose my mind. I almost wrote on his Facebook *"Guess what? I got a silver dollar and a pair of socks! Who needs you?"* But, I refrained. I know at some point I paid the check and drove home, although I have no recollection of any of it.

Amy was organizing the girls' shoes by the door when I barged in. She glanced up. "No show?"

I shook my head. "I had to try." I told her about Marty's Facebook Check-In. "I guess that's my answer," I said. Not only was it a big fat *get lost*, it was a *get lost, dumbass.* "I can't be the crazy ex-girlfriend," I said. "I can't keep chasing them. I have to stop."

But I didn't know how to stop. Every morning, every night, they were on my mind. I ran through scenarios where if I could just say this or if I could just talk to her or if he would just agree to meet me once . . . I wanted to fix it. Regardless of what everyone was telling me, Marty's words had sunk into the tiny cracks in my heart and broke it that much more. I was the reason why this family was suffering. I was the reason why Ed and Bev's marriage was rattled.

You're tearing my family apart!

I was the one who broke it, so I was the one who needed to repair it. And I had no idea how.

"They hate us," Catey said, one night after dinner.

I shook my head. "They don't hate us. You can't hate somebody you don't know."

"It feels like they hate us," she replied.

It did. It felt like they hated everything about us. Especially the fact that we existed at all.

"I'm not writing Marty back," I announced a week later. "I'm not going to write any of them ever again!"

That lasted three months. I didn't exactly write them but I sent all of them—the entire Schneyder family—including Marty, Edward/Bev, and the three boys—a Christmas card.

Adam's card was the only one returned. I wasn't surprised. I figured he was still in rehab and I assumed I didn't have his correct address but it was worth a shot. I had heard through the grapevine that after my letters to Mark and Kevin were received, that Edward and Bev drove to visit with Adam and they told him about me. I was glad to hear this. It was important for them to tell someone, to present their side of the story. Even if I was portrayed in a bad light, I was happy to know that they finally had to speak about me to someone else.

I was also told that after receiving the letter I had mailed in August that their youngest son, Kevin, went to his parents and proposed to them that they throw a BBQ and invite the family over. "Introduce him and his family to your family," was the rumor I heard he suggested. I also understood that he found out from his mother that none of those things would be happening and that Kevin's idea was immediately squashed.

I was beginning my spiral into black, drinking way more than usual. Instead of the one drink to relax after work, I was now drinking for medicinal purposes. Two drinks a night became three. Three drinks became four. And it was a consistent seven out of seven days a week.

"Maybe you should see a therapist," Amy suggested.

"I am currently practicing alcohol therapy," I told her.

To top things off, within one terrible week in October, my dad lost his oldest brother, John, and a few days later, his mother, my Grandma Peterson. She had been my last living grandparent.

Amy, the girls, and I attended Uncle John's funeral. I hadn't seen any of my Blair relatives for years. I calculated that it had been at least fifteen years since I had seen John and a good five to ten years since I had laid eyes on most of the people there. My girls were meeting many of them for the first time.

During a quiet moment, I spotted my Uncle Greg, my dad's younger brother. I recalled from the anonymous book we received that his brother-in-law, Bruce Richter, was good friends with Edward. Amy and I decided to approach him. After a few pleasantries, Amy sprung it on him, throwing it out like a fastball, because if we didn't do it now, the moment might pass us by.

"Michael had something exciting happen this year," Amy began. "He found his biological father."

My Uncle Greg straightened. His attention became more focused. "He did?"

"Yes." Amy nodded. "In fact, I think the man has an odd connection to someone you know."

"Oh? Who is that?"

"Do you know Bruce Richter?"

"He's my brother-in-law." Greg seemed alarmed.

Amy put a hand up. "Don't worry, Bruce is not Michael's biological father."

Greg relaxed. "Okay."

"But a good friend of his is. A man named Edward Schneyder."

Greg blinked. It was long and slow. "Ed Schneyder?" He paused and then asked, "From Lawrence?"

I could feel the sizzle between the three of us, that rubber band-like feeling returning, connecting us with tension. "Yes," Amy replied.

"Yeah, I know him," Greg said very nonchalant. "I've dealt with lots of the Schneyders over the years. I used to take all my cars over to them to get fixed. Mostly I dealt with the oldest brother, Don. But, I know Ed. I have known him for . . . I don't know, maybe thirty years."

Amy and I stared at him. All we could do was breathe. My uncle knew my biological father for thirty years? Was this just a weird coincidence? Or was there more?

Then my Uncle Greg looked me up and down, like it was the first time he had ever seen me. "I should have put it together. Of course you're related to them. You look just like them." He nodded. "I can't believe I missed it. You are all Schneyder."

THIRTY-EIGHT

When I was sixteen my mom and I rode our bicycles up to the grocery store. I had received the bike at the beginning of June and the weather was now beginning to turn colder so my mom and I thought one more, long bike ride was what was needed that day. Our local grocery store was a couple of miles away. We rode up to the store, shopped around, and we started back home.

There was a point in our ride where I broke away from my mom and decided to ride rogue through a gravel parking lot. I got some decent speed going when I noticed what I thought was a dip in the gravel. I hit it. The next thing I remember I was waking up in the hospital with my family surrounding me.

My mom was nervous. She was pacing the floor.

"Hey, there he is." My dad's voice said from somewhere.

"Hi-ya, honey." That was Grandma.

My eyes followed the room. Grandpa in the corner, my mom pacing the floor, my dad by the window, Grandma at my bedside. With exception of my grandma, they were all looking away from me. But they were there.

Grandma reached over and held my hand. "Don't try to talk," she told me. She smiled sweetly, like she would do when I was sick. Like, real, real sick.

My mom was fussing over a plastic cup, wrapped in plastic. It took a few tries but she freed the cup and filled it with water. She jabbed a straw in it and placed the straw in my mouth. "Drink some."

I tried to suck on the straw but couldn't. She positioned the cup directly to my lips. I slurped some water. Most of it went down my neck and chest. "Back to the swabs," I heard her say and suddenly a soft, squishy fabric held by a stick was being thrust against my lips. I put my hand up and shoved it away.

Something had happened.

I grabbed the swab and threw it. "Wha' happen'd?" That was really hard to say.

They all exchanged nervous looks. My mom spoke up, "You had an accident."

I pressed my head into my pillow and closed my eyes. I remembered riding my bike with my mom. "Car?" I asked. "Car hi' me?"

My mom shook her head. "No, you fell off your bike."

Yes, I remembered the bike, I wanted to tell her. "Wha' happen'd?"

"You hit a pothole in the parking lot and your front tire flew off the bike. You went face first into the gravel," she told me. "You skidded quite a ways... about twenty feet on the gravel."

I remembered the gravel. Even now I could almost taste it.

"You lost consciousness," she continued. "We had to call an ambulance."

"You crashed in the right spot," my grandma added. "The fire station was across the street and there were firemen eating supper outside. They saw it happen and raced over to you."

"They did?" That must have been cool, me all bloody and shit. I wished I could remember some of it.

Grandma continued, "The ambulance brought you in and the doctors took you immediately in to surgery."

Surgery? I looked at my body. Nothing seemed broken. I was covered in a pale yellow blanket. I wiggled my toes and moved my legs around. They moved with ease. I could see my arms and hands.

Besides some scrapes and bruises, they looked fine. "Surg'ry?"

My grandma held my gaze. "Yes. That was two days ago. We've been so scared."

Two days?

Just then a tall man in a white lab coat knocked on my door. "Hey!" He announced, in a pleasant voice. "He's awake!"

My family started immediate chatter with the man. It was obvious this was my doctor and from the things they were saying, he was my surgeon. "How are you feeling?" He asked me.

I shrugged. "Okay."

"Good." He smiled. "You are a lucky guy. That fall you took could have been much worse."

The way he used the word "fall" made me feel like I was an elderly person. *Grandma took a fall today,* like it was a serious thing. Hell, I fell all the time. I had fallen a hundred times off my bike in the past. I frowned. That kind of hurt.

"Everything is scheduled for the morning," he said, to my mother. "Should take about two hours." He looked back to me. "If you're hungry, you better eat something for dinner. No food or drink for you after midnight."

"Why?" I asked.

"You're having surgery in the morning."

That was strange. I thought I had already had surgery. I had a lot of questions I wanted to ask, but when I opened my mouth to speak, nothing seemed to happen so I mumbled, "'Nother one?"

My grandma's raspy voice filled the quiet room. "He wants to know why he's having another surgery."

I nodded. Again I looked down at my body. It looked intact. I placed my hands over my abdomen and pressed down. It didn't hurt. In fact, my stomach growled back with hunger. The nagging ring of my mom's voice popped up in the back of my brain, *"Face first into the gravel ...*"

All eyes went to the surgeon so I looked at him, too.

"You need two surgeries," he explained. "When you first came in, we performed emergency surgery, which was the first of your facial reconstruction."

Facial reconstruction. The words were still lingering in my head as he continued. "When you landed with your bike —"

My mind raced. I remembered the bike ride. I could see the parking lot. I pedaled faster and faster, my hair whipped away from my face, and I hit that dip in the gravel—

"Your tire popped off and you landed on your face."

I remembered hitting something hard and the momentum of my body surging forward and, then, nothing. Until I woke up in the hospital.

"You skidded across the road about twenty feet. The left side of your face detached from here," he placed a finger under his left eye, "to here." He made a wiggle line down his cheek, toward his nose, through the middle of his lips, and over to the bottom of his chin. "Your cheekbone is crushed and your jaw is busted. We scooped two cups of gravel out of your mouth and the insides of your skin. When you skidded, your flesh ripped away from your face, exposing your bones, and all that has to be pieced back together again. Tomorrow we're going to finish you up. We have to do some skin grafts. I'm cutting some sections of skin from here," he turned around and patted his ass. "I will take as little as possible but I need to take some sizes like this." He made a triangle with his hands.

He stopped talking and smiled at me.

"My bu'?" I tried to say.

"You can't talk very well," the surgeon explained. "We wired your jaw shut."

I reached up and touched my face. Gently. I could feel bandages and a wire. *Facial reconstruction.* I tried hard to make my words clear, "My bu-tt?"

The surgeon nodded, "Your gluteus is a very fleshy part of your body and taking sections from it is ideal because it's a large, smooth area."

I couldn't believe what I was hearing. I'm sixteen years old and a doctor has just told me that not only was my face a jigsaw puzzle, that to fix it, they were going to have to cut skin off my ass.

I was freaking out.

The surgeon walked over to my bed and pushed my call light. "I will have the nurse give you something to sleep," he told me. I felt my grandma's hand squeeze mine. A nurse appeared and hovered over my bed with a syringe. She tugged on my IV tubing and I watched as she pushed the needle in. Soon I drifted off to sleep.

When I woke up again, it was the next evening. My mom was in my room. "Hey," she said. She was walking around my room, pinning get well cards onto a cork board.

I blinked and pushed up off my pillow. "Hey." My mouth didn't move, though. I reached up and felt my face. Bandages. Wires. I tried to sit up higher and I felt pain radiate from behind me. My ass!

"Surgery was this morning. You've been asleep all day," she told me. She pointed to a pad and pen, sitting on my bedside table. "You're not supposed to talk. If you need anything, write it down."

I sat there for a moment and tried to think of what I wanted to say.

"The surgery went well," she continued, her back to me. "The doctor said you will heal up just like new." She pinned up a home-made card from my sisters. "I can't believe that happened. I can't believe what I saw. I will never get that image of seeing you like that out of my head."

I blinked. I tapped the pen on the notepad until she turned around and then I pointed at her purse.

"What?" she asked.

I turned the notebook around and wrote *Mirror.*

"I don't have a mirror," my mom replied.

I frowned. She was saying this to me with perfect makeup on. Her lipstick had been freshly applied. I underlined the word *mirror* and raised my eyebrows at her.

"I don't have a mirror with me," she repeated.

That was bullshit. I threw the pen down and looked away.

My mom stayed her distance. She walked over and rearranged some flowers that were nearby. I wondered who they were from but I didn't ask. "You should only have to be here for a few days. Everything went really well. You shouldn't need any more surgeries."

Fucking bike! I wanted to yell, but what was the point? I couldn't talk, let alone yell. The television came on. I turned the volume up and kept my focus on whatever crap was on and tried my best to disregard my mother.

"Do you want me to order you food?" She showed me a paper menu. "Do you want to circle what you want?" I ignored her. "Okay..." she picked up the pen I had thrown. "I will choose something for you."

Later in the evening, when I was alone, the door opened, and a woman walked in with my food tray. My mom ordered a cheeseburger and fries. It came as a puréed shake. I took a sip and almost vomited. My stomach heaved and my jaw clenched. The pain was horrible. I ran into the bathroom, just in case. I turned on the light and as my eyes adjusted, I immediately noticed that the mirror above the sink had been removed. I looked around. There were no mirrors anywhere. I bent down close to the toilet and tried to catch my reflection in the handle. I bent over the sink and tried to see it in the faucet. All I could see was a distorted blob.

I was in the hospital for a few more days. If I took a walk, a nurse aid went with me. The staff purposely steered me away from anything reflective. It was aggravating. Every day the nurses changed bandages. I watched white pieces of gauze caked in dried blood and yellow goo being removed from my face. They replaced the bandages until the third day when the surgeon said it was time for my face to be exposed to direct air.

"It looks good," he assured me. "Just a couple more days and you will be able to go home."

I pointed to my jaw.

"We will remove the wires before you leave," he said. "You won't be able to eat solid foods for a while, but you'll be able to talk better."

My family visited frequently. My mom worked at the hospital, so she stopped in on her lunch breaks, bringing me sodas and drawing pads. My dad came in every other evening, in between his jobs. My grandparents came in and brought my sisters, and my Aunt Susan came in with my two cousins.

"Oh, my god," my cousin Lisa said. She made a gagging sound. "Your face is ugly."

I glared at her. "So is yours," I spat.

A few days in, a group of my friends came in to visit. They brought me a Rubik's Cube and Mad Magazines. They stared at me for a long time, their eyes not able to disguise anything. Finally, Jason spoke up, "Well, guess we got a new nickname for you: Scarface." He laughed. And, thankfully, so did the other guys.

I laughed, too, even though it hurt like hell.

It was getting close for me to go home. The surgeon had kept me a couple more days because of an infection but finally he came in and told me, "Tomorrow we will remove the wires and if all goes well, you'll go home the next day."

That was exciting news. To celebrate, I ordered three milkshakes for breakfast. I finished two when the dietary aide came in and removed my tray. I reached over to pull the bedside table closer to me when the top of it moved. I hadn't noticed that before. I rolled it to my chest and pushed it lightly. The top of the table slid back and underneath were two hidden compartments. One was a cubby which was labeled "makeup"; the other side was flat and there was a button that said "mirror." I didn't hesitate. I pushed the button and a small mirror popped up.

My face reflected back to me. I stared at myself. When the surgeon said *"Piece things back together,"* he wasn't kidding. My face was literally patched in places, trails of stitches connected my skin, making everything taut. I touched the stitches. They looked like tiny ants, crawling all over my face. I looked like Frankenstein's monster. And with that I mean, I looked like a science experiment. Who was this guy? This was not me. This was some messed-up version of what I used to look like. I was the things nightmares were made of.

I tried to slow my breathing. I felt like I might hyperventilate and with a jaw wired shut—I was pretty sure that would be a very bad idea. The wire was inside and outside my mouth. It had hurt before but now that I could actually see it, the wire suddenly felt like it was slowly suffocating me.

I can't breathe, I thought. This isn't real. I can't breathe. I wanted the wires out *now!* I have to walk around with these stitches dancing across my face? I have to go to school like this?

I glanced around the room. Where was my mom? Oh, my God . . . Where was Grandma? I needed to slow my breathing down. Where was my dad?

I looked back into the mirror and through the scars, the stitches, and the wires, I found my eyes. They looked like they belonged to a stranger. And I wondered, like I always had, who are you? Whose face is that now? It's not your mom's and it's not your dad's. It's not even yours anymore.

I blinked and tears fell down my repulsive face.

THIRTY-NINE

From the beginning, we are shaped by the things that we know about ourselves and by the things we don't know. These things combined are the formation of who we become. The morals and values that are instilled in us are based on what we believe is true about our lives versus what we know to be untrue. When we are misled, however, information that we *think* is true about ourselves and then finding out that it isn't true at all, well ... forming a person that way can be dangerous.

During those times in my teens, after the accident and then again when I was eighteen and kicked out of my house, the thought of suicide was not far from my mind. Looking back, I think I took comfort in the thought *"If things don't go well, if you can't handle it, there's always an option."* I used it like a warm blanket. Pills or carbon monoxide poisoning. I had thought about it enough that I knew I couldn't kill myself using too much violence. I didn't have the stomach for that.

I felt alone in the life my parents had created for me, but I held onto the fact that I was young, I had my whole life ahead of me. I didn't have my own family, no wife, no kids, no pets, not even a plant. I was tethered to nothing. Everything I owned could be stuffed into a duffel bag.

I could walk out the door and start living my own life or I could cash in my chips and swallow an entire bottle of Tylenol PM.

Should I stay or should I go?

I fell into my old habit and made a Don't Kill Myself list. There were three things that stopped me from forming a more detailed suicide plan:

1. Get out of this house/town
2. My grandma loved me
3. Find out who my bio-father is

I held onto this silly thought that finding my biological father would solve my riddle. I thought having his name, seeing a photo, knowing that he existed would bring things full circle for me. What I didn't expect was that instead, I would stand in front of a mirror, looking at my reflection asking the same question that had haunted me for forty-six years, "Who am I?"

Because my narrative about who I thought I was had, once again, changed.

Staring at myself I didn't see the scars from my accident anymore. Time and a fantastic plastic surgeon had caused them to fade until they blended so well that the only person who really saw them was Amy when she kissed me. There were tiny moments where the light would hit my face just right and she would trace a line from my nose, through my lips, down to my chin. "I see it," she would say.

I could see hints of my mother in my face. I could catch glimmers of my Grandma Lang. But now, 90% of my reflection was Edward. I grabbed my toothbrush and brushed my teeth, keeping my eyes down. Any glimpse made me sick. I checked myself in the long bedroom mirror, making sure my buttons were straight and my shirt was tucked in properly. I'd catch a quick peek of myself and my mind would flash to Edward's car, sitting in his front seat, both of us removing our sunglasses. *Let me get a good look at ya ... yeah, you're mine.*

I continued through my days as if I was an actor playing the role of Michael Blair. Maybe I was. Maybe I had been an actor my entire life, pretending to be some guy who I wasn't. I was born Michael Lang. I was adopted into Michael Blair. My bloodline led to Michael Schneyder. Two of those people didn't exist and yet all three of those people were wrapped up inside me.

In the evening, I continued to drink. A lot. On the weekends, I drank. A lot more. My mood was up and down. I didn't sleep during the night and during the day I wasn't really awake. Christmas 2017 had come and gone. It was good, I guess. I don't remember what we did with Amy's family and I don't remember what we did with mine.

The winter months were like a blur in time. Wake up in the morning, get dressed and do whatever I was supposed to do on this planet—teach or design something, pretend to be interested in whatever one of the girls was telling me, eat, drink, sleep, force a smile when someone showed concern, deny, deny, hide and stuff things down deep. Deeper. The next day, repeat.

I knew Amy was worried. She would watch me quietly from across the room, tracking my moves, asking if she could get something for me. She was careful with questions and shushed the girls a lot, "Keep it down tonight. Your dad needs to sleep."

Weirdly, I woke up at every little sound. I already suffered from insomnia and whether it was my drinking or worrying, my insomnia was cranked up a notch. I felt like I was going to crawl out of my skin. I was going crazy.

I opened a blank sheet of paper and started another Don't Kill Myself list. But I didn't write anything down. I already knew my reasons for staying alive were Amy and the girls but I couldn't bring myself to add their names to a list like that.

One dark night in January, we sat down to eat dinner. Amy made a pot roast with potatoes. It wasn't her best.

"Are you okay?" she asked, watching me eat.

"I don't know."

Amy rephrased. "How was your day?"

"I don't know."

There was a pause and I glanced up to see Amy staring at me. She looked alarmed. "What's wrong?"

I had no words to offer her to explain what I was going through. She would never understand it. "I don't feel like I'm here. I know my body is sitting here but I don't feel real."

Amy reached across the table and pinched my arm. "You're real," she said, assertively.

I put my fork down. "Every time I look in a mirror, I see him staring back at me. I fucked up and I can't fix it. I can't go forward, I can't go backwards. I can't sleep because I close my eyes and I dream of him. I can't write him. I can't call him. I'm part of him and he doesn't want me. And all I want to do is drive my car off of a bridge. Every morning I leave for work, I drive by the perfect spot. Or, I don't know, I could take my entire bottle of Ambien. Maybe then I will finally sleep."

I couldn't read the expression on Amy's face. I had never seen it before.

I shrugged. "I just want to walk out the door, walk out of this world and just disappear."

Amy swallowed. "Why do you think you feel that way?"

Was she high? I frowned. "Amy, don't you get it? I should have never been born. Everything I do, I just cause pain to people. To my mother, to my dad, to Edward and Bev. I probably ruined their marriage." I paused. "This whole year ... Edward and Marty and ... my brothers ..." I trailed off. "They didn't just break my heart, they broke my spirit."

"You need to talk to somebody," Amy finally breathed. "Like, you know, a professional."

I picked up my fork. "The hell I am."

The next day, Amy sent the girls out for ice cream and sat down next to me. "Michael, you are going to talk to someone." A demand, this time. "If I have to take you in and commit you to a psych ward, I will. But first, let's try a less dramatic approach and find you a counselor."

I started with my doctor, who knew me well. I walked in, told her my sad story and where things were now. She sat down. "Well, shit. You're by far my more interesting patient I've had in here today." She gave me a referral to the clinic social worker and made an appointment for me the following day.

I had a long break on my lunch hour and ran over to talk to my new counselor. I sat across from a lovely young lady, mid-twenties, with a certificate above her head which stated she graduated two years before. I told her my story. She nodded a few times and when I was finished she asked, "Do you think you drink enough water?"

I shrugged. "Yeah, I drink four of these a day." I held up my Yeti. It was true. I had been drinking sixty-four ounces of water a day for at least ten years. "It's how I maintain my amazing figure," I joked.

"Hmmm . . ." she seemed to be in deep thought. "I think you need to add another eight ounces." Then she pulled a prescription pad out and wrote me a script to add another eight ounces of H2o to my daily drinking routine.

When I got home, Amy didn't balk. "Find another therapist."

I pulled out my computer and did some researching. There was a guy not too far away from where I lived that looked like he might work. I called his office and met with him two days later.

Rodney was a six foot six, three hundred pound, African American guy who was probably a year or two older than me. I walked in his office and looked around. Everything had a place and looked nice and tidy, except for his desk, which was stacked with books, loose papers, and old coffee cups. I smiled.

Rodney didn't hold a writing utensil, there was no notepad anywhere, and nothing seemed to be recording us. His hands rested loosely across his middle. "What brings you in today?" he asked.

I took a breath and told him. From the beginning, being raised by my mom, to the adoption, through the secrets and lies, the search, the failure, the DNA tests, the results, the discovery, the meeting, the rejection, the aunts, the love, my parents' reaction, the feeling of hopelessness, the drinking, the sadness, the hurt, the feeling of unworthiness, the thoughts of suicide. I took a breath. I could see Rodney was letting everything wash over him. "Oh," I added, "and my grandma died two months ago."

Rodney sat back in his chair and rubbed his hands together. He gently said, "Man, that was heavy. I can't believe you've been walking around with all of this on your shoulders." He nodded. "Anyone would be at a breaking point."

Breaking point. I hadn't thought of it that way but it was true. I had been white-knuckling it for months now.

"What word would you use to describe yourself after coming out of all of this?" Rodney asked.

I thought about it and said the first word that popped in my head. "I feel like a failure."

Rodney nodded. "Failure is a feeling long before it becomes a result."

I swallowed. That made sense to me.

After spending a few weeks reading the list of Don't Kill Yourself books that Rodney had suggested, he turned his attention back to the task at hand: closure.

Closure was a big thing to Rodney. I needed to find a path to peace. My problem was I didn't know how. That's why I was here, wasn't it? I told myself that I opened my heart to receive any outcome possible but the truth was my heart was open to the best outcome possible. Now that I hadn't achieved that, I had to find a way to close my heart but how does one do that when you already opened it and now it was profusely bleeding out?

"How was Rodney today?" Amy asked me as I came into the kitchen. She was chopping up cucumbers. I had been seeing Rodney for a couple of months.

"He wore green today." Every visit I had, Rodney wore a cardigan with leather patches on his elbows. Every time it was a different color. I wondered how many of these sweaters he owned. I imagined he had a closet full of them.

"What color of green?"

"Olive," I replied.

Amy nodded. She smiled. I think she thought I was doing better. I hadn't asked. The last time I asked her, she replied that I was "scary." That was three weeks ago.

"Rodney wants me to write another letter."

Amy sighed and paused her chopping. "I don't know. Another letter? Where have letters gotten us?"

"Yeah, I get it." I did. I had been thinking the same thing.

"You may as well write a letter and then burn it. All you do is write letters, mail them out, and who the hell knows what happens to them? Those idiots probably get them and don't even open them up. They just toss them in the trash." Amy chopped again. "Maybe you should, I don't know...pick up the phone and just call one of them."

That was easier said than done. It was one of those things that you brag that you're going to do and then when you get to the actual moment, you chicken out. I had told myself numerous times that all I had to do was make a phone call. But when I started plugging in a number, my finger suddenly froze. I looked at Amy and she returned the look but her face changed, like she said something wrong. She had been extra careful with her word usage lately. She immediately followed with, "You should do whatever you're comfortable with."

"Rodney thinks I should write Bev."

"What are you going to say to her?"

I shrugged. "I'm sorry."

"Don't you tell her you're sorry." Amy pointed the knife at me. "What are you sorry for? That her husband chose to have sex with a girl—more than three years before he married his wife? What are you sorry for? Being born? Spitting in a tube? Wanting to know your father? Like she . . ." Amy shook her head and went back to chopping. "You know what, this is your thing. You write what you want, but, please, whatever you do, don't tell her you're sorry."

"Tell me what you really think," I kidded. I ate a couple of the cucumbers. "There is something that I've been kicking around," I casually mentioned.

"What's that?"

I smiled. "Saying fuck it and rip off the Band-Aid."

Amy put the knife down. "What does that mean?"

It was a crazy idea. I locked eyes with her and grinned. "Let the cat out of the bag. Tell all of them."

FORTY

Edward was one of ten kids.

Out of his nine siblings, I was talking with two, Louisa and Carolyn. When I originally spoke to Louisa about my DNA results, she mentioned she had talked things over with her sister, Mary. That left Helen and Judy, neither of whom knew about me. Edward also had four brothers. I knew Louisa originally had called Wayne, thinking he could be my biological father, so he knew about me. I had already encountered the ups and downs of Marty. I also heard through the grapevine that Edward's brother Bill had learned secondhand about me. That left Don who, as far as I knew, did not know. It also left many cousins.

"I can rip off the Band-Aid and tell all of them," I said to Amy. "I was thinking of sending out an announcement, kind of like a birth announcement. But I want it to be unique. I need it to stand out."

What I came up with was unconventional. I brought Amy and the girls into the studio and took their individual photos. I had them pose in exaggerated waves and surprised facial expressions and made them mouth "Hello." I then gave the camera to Rosie and had her take photos of me doing the same.

I designed a 3-dimensioned pop-up cube to send in the mail. On the front a simple, "Hello, There!" and on the inside, a brief statement about why the recipient was receiving the card. When the person opened the envelope, it activated the cube tucked away inside that popped out of the folds. Each side of the cube contained a picture of each of us, waving or saying hello. Our names were written under our faces. Inside the card, I explained to the recipient that we had a DNA connection and I was related to the Schneyder Family. I included a link to a website that I also designed. The person could go on the website and read more about my journey, the DNA results, a "Meet the Blairs" section, and the many ways they could contact me, if they desired.

When I told my friends what I was doing, I got two responses—either I was 'gutsy" or I was "stupid." I suppose I was a little bit of both.

When the cards arrived from the printer, Amy and I tested it out. It worked perfect. I took it out of the envelope, opened the card, the cube activated and exploded out of the folds. It bopped me in the nose. I laughed. That was exactly what I was going for—I wanted Edward to get this in the mail, open it up, and BOOP! A big picture of me, smacking him in the face.

I never considered not sending Edward the announcement. Even though he made it perfectly clear that he wanted nothing more to do with me, I still wanted him to know that I was moving forward and how I was doing it. I didn't want him in the dark. I wanted to keep him in the know because I wasn't going to keep secrets from him.

I sent the card to the entire family—twenty-two cousins, five aunts, four uncles, three half-brothers, one biological father, and a partridge in a pear tree.

"How do you think Edward will react?" Amy asked.

I knew exactly what he was going to do. The minute he opened his card, he was going to go into damage control mode. He would either call or drive around to visit his siblings and tell them his story—whatever it was now. He would throw me under the bus as fast as he could and claim I was the bad guy and he was the good guy. He would ask them to not contact me. *I'm the victim in all of this.*

"He told me the only two people he was allowed to talk to about everything was me and Bev," I said, remembering Edward's words. "Now he will be able to talk to whoever in the family he wants. He won't have to hide anymore."

Eighteen months had passed since I first discovered Edward. This time, I didn't hesitate sending the announcement out, like I had when I mailed my first letter. This felt different. When I sent my original letter to Edward, it was from me to him. This announcement was from my family to my family.

Coming out of the first year, out of the first long, depressing winter, I was surprised at how strong I felt. Rodney helped with that, he was encouraging me to remember why I started this process in the first place. He helped me find my voice, to stay true to my core. I also started assisting the Adoptees Coalition of Iowa, to help achieve their main goal, to change the Right to Know law so that adoptees could obtain their original birth certificates. Through them, I started talking to more and more adoptees and NPEs. I discovered the number of people like me was growing because of the easy accessibility of DNA test kits. There were many people who were in all age groups—from their twenties to their nineties, spitting in tubes just for fun and finding out that their father who raised them wasn't their biological father. And no one had bothered telling them. Through their own investigations, many found that several family members knew all along and had kept the secret from them.

It made me grateful that I found out the truth when I was eighteen. My mom didn't ever have to tell me. She could have kept the charade going forever, if she wanted. I listened to the stories of these people and I nodded along. It might have taken her eighteen years, but in the end, my mother did the right thing.

One night, Amy and I invited our friend, Rochelle, over for dinner. Rochelle was adopted by her parents when she was two months old.

Amy and I have known Rochelle for more than twenty years and when I started my journey, Amy sent Rochelle a text telling her that I had found my bio-father and how we had done it. Rochelle quickly texted back a photo of an AncestryDNA kit that she ordered for herself. It had arrived that day in the mail. We were privileged to walk alongside Rochelle during her own journey. Amy gave her pointers that we had found helpful and Rochelle gave us websites and Facebook groups that were helpful to me.

The day Rochelle received her DNA results, she called Amy. Using Ancestry, Google, and Facebook, they zeroed in on the identity of Rochelle's mother. It took them fifteen minutes. Her father's identity was known by the end of the day. Rochelle contacted her bio-mother and, because she figured out her father was killed in Vietnam six months after Rochelle was born, she sent a letter to her paternal bio-grandmother and bio-aunt.

It turned out that Amy and Rochelle had found the right people. Rochelle's paternal side was ecstatic. Everyone on her father's side had always known about her and were in full knowledge of Rochelle being given up for adoption. Her father was killed at the age of twenty and never married nor had any other children. Having Rochelle in their life was like having a piece of her bio-father back with them again.

Rochelle's bio-mom held out for a while. As with many birth mothers, she was still carrying the wounds of her secret baby. She had confided in her husband years before but had never told their children. She was afraid of the shock it would bring. When Rochelle's mother finally told them, they handled it with grace and curiosity. Rochelle and her bio-mother began the reunion process, along with her half-siblings. Rochelle was able to meet both sides of her bio-families and was welcomed with open arms. Rochelle ended up getting what so many adoptees long for—love, acceptance, and family.

At dinner, I told Rochelle about the announcement. "They're stamped and ready. I'm going to mail them out in a couple of days." I gave her a sample card and had her open it up. POP! The cube exploded and hit Rochelle in the face.

"Go for it." She laughed.

I made Rochelle a vodka lemonade. Amy was seated to her right, I was to her left. "I'm a little nervous," I admitted.

"That's because it's a nerve-racking thing." Rochelle stirred her drink. "People don't understand that this is not fun for us. This sucks. This is trauma. We're conditioned to think of adoption as a fairytale where this baby grows in a new mother's heart and all that shit—and that's great—but what people don't realize is that on the other side of that, someone had to give their baby away. Your father *abandoned you* when your mom was pregnant." Rochelle took a drink. "I was supposed to be born to a different family than the one I was raised in. You were, too. There's trauma in that. People don't like to view adoption under that light."

I had mixed feelings about that. I understood where Rochelle was coming from but I also had amazing friends who had adopted children and were now a family. Technically, I was half-adopted—raised by a biological and an adopted parent. In some ways, I had the best of both worlds. Being with my maternal grandparents and my Aunt Susan was like peanut butter and jelly. We went together. Bonding with my Blair relatives required work. I understood what Rochelle was saying—it was the age-old question of nature versus nurture.

In utero, during those nine months of gestation, we are designed by genetic codes and wired to belong to those two people. At birth, we are preprogrammed to be part of our mother's family and our father's family. We are the half of their whole. When a person is given up for adoption or when a parent is nonexistent in the raising of the child, not only does the child suffer from the void, the family they were supposed to be part of has a gaping hole.

Nurture is where an adoptive parent can shine. It's when a parent enhances the uniqueness of their child to guide and enable that person to be the best they can be. Adoptive parents are at a disadvantage as the child they brought home is not genetically theirs so it's just as much a surprise to them as it is to everyone else what their child is predisposed to. As humans we need both, nature and nurture.

Rarely is adoption a *Little Orphan Annie* story. Adoption is a complicated and strange concept. A baby is removed from their biological relatives, their name is changed, their true existence is hidden, and all paperwork leading back to where they originated is locked away. And most adoptees, no matter how old they are, are never granted their own birth certificate. They are not allowed the right to hear their own origin story.

I have talked to many adoptees who waited too long to search because their adoptive parents told them they didn't want them to ever look for their bio-families. So the adoptees waited until their adoptive parents passed away and then discovered that their own bio-parents had also died. They missed each other. Adoptive parents need to be realistic. One day their child may want to go and search for their original family. This has nothing to do with lack of love or respect for the parents who raised them. This has to do with a longing, a void that was created at birth, a need to know answers to questions that they need answered.

"I know I'm supposed to be thankful," Rochelle said. "I'm supposed to be the grateful adoptee but sometimes I get so mad. I missed out on so many good times and getting to know these people from the very beginning. I didn't get to meet a lot of people. Now I have to meet them in photographs. Everyone else has memories with these people. I don't and never will. I feel like I will never fit in."

I nodded. "I get that. With me, it's like I'm working from the ground up and trying to worm my way up this family and maybe one day I'll reach Edward again. Then I will get to meet my brothers." I glanced at Rochelle. She got it. "I do worry that sending these announcements out will cause more disruption in their family."

Rochelle shrugged. "Haven't you already done that?"

"Yeah," I admitted. I had. "When I sent my original letter out to Edward, I told him I didn't want to disrupt his family and here I am—"

"Here you are, what?" Rochelle challenged. "The minute Edward read that letter you disrupted his life. I know that's what people are supposed to say that they don't want to disrupt lives but it happens. I mean, what are you supposed to do? Live the rest of your life knowing that you have the technical advances at your fingertips to find your biological father and not find him? You're supposed to walk around with this question mark over your head forever? What about you? Don't you deserve the right to reach out? Your family is exactly that—yours. They're adults. Let them make up their own minds. You don't need his permission for anything. He made that clear last year when he let you go, and he made that clear forty-six years ago. He has walked away from you twice. You have the right to make your own pathway. They're his family but they're your family, too."

I lifted my glass to Rochelle and she clinked hers against mine. "I like you more and more," I said. "To family."

"To family," she agreed.

I took a drink. "So, things are going well with you?"

"Yeah."

"You've met your mom and siblings?"

"Yup."

"And your dad's side? You're moving forward with them?"

"I talk to them every week," she said.

"That's awesome," I smiled. "So, how are you doing?"

Rochelle sighed. "Oh, you know . . . I'm in therapy."

"Hey! Me, too!" I shouted.

Then we laughed so hard that we almost cried.

FORTY-ONE

Marty's text message had really gotten to me. It had been nine months since he had sent it but his words had stayed with me to the point that I pretty much memorized the entire thing. *You're tearing my family apart* kept me up for more than a few nights.

As time went on, however, I started to deconstruct his words and I focused on two different lines: *And why would you ever want to meet with Louisa? You have nothing to gain in meeting her!*

Deciding to make the announcements and send them out came from those two lines. Instead of deterring me, Marty's words became the driving force guiding me to make the announcement. What did I have to gain? Aunts, uncles, cousins. Family. History learned and a future shared.

Marty's proposed question was incomplete, though. If you're going to ask what did I have to gain, you should also ask what did I have to lose? The answer to that was easy: nothing and no one. I had already lost him.

It didn't take long to begin hearing from relatives after the announcements went out. One on a Thursday, another on a Saturday. It was a slow trickle for a couple of months. I received phone calls and Facebook messages, some openly requesting to be my friend and others who wanted to stay anonymous. However my new relative wanted to handle things was fine with me, I wasn't going to push. Many wanted to meet. So Amy, the three girls, I and reserved one weekend a month, which we designated *Schneyder Reunion Weekend*. We traveled all over to meet family again and again and again.

The first one to reach out was my new aunt, Judy Schneyder. She was sarcastic, salt of the earth, and didn't give a flying fuck about keeping secrets. Through her hard exterior, she let me and my family in to get to know her tender interior. She is the kind of person who looks you in the eye and tells the story like it is, whether you want to hear it or not.

We learned my instincts had been correct and that after Edward had received the announcement, he drove around town and called on his siblings to do damage control.

Aunt Judy told me, "Ed showed up here, the Sunday after I got your card. Actually, the day he showed up was Father's Day."

My breath hitched and my chest grew tight. It wasn't lost on me that my biological father spent his own Father's Day asking his siblings to not speak to his son. How ironic.

Judy went on, "Ed sat with me on my deck and talked with me about you. He had your announcement with him and he said, 'Michael designed this. He's very talented.' He said it like he was *proud* of you."

This surprised me and I didn't know how to feel or react. I opened my mouth but nothing came out.

"You didn't miss anything," Judy said, lighting a cigarette. Amy and I were sitting on her deck, watching cars go by her house. "There's not much to any of them. They'll lie to your face and leave you on the side of the road for dead."

I frowned, listening to her. I wasn't sure exactly who she was speaking of. She talked in general terms but it sounded personal.

"You were probably better off without any of 'em." Her eyes wandered over and met mine. "Like I said, you didn't miss much."

"Yeah, I did," I replied. "I missed all of it."

Judy shook her head, mumbled something under her breath and then piped up. "Ed told me the story of how he met your mother and that he had his underwear on—"

"He's still telling that story?" Amy and I both yelled out together. Even our girls laughed.

"I'm sorry," I said. "We don't mean to react like that. We just thought he would have changed his story by now. I mean, who would believe it?"

Judy replied, "He only has to convince one person."

I nodded. Another one who got it.

"It's such a bullshit story, but that's Ed for you. He will do whatever he needs to in order to save his own ass. He's cheap and I mean, dirt cheap. He won't buy an onion at the grocery store if he thinks it costs ten cents too much. He probably thinks you're out to get his money."

A different relative said the same thing. "I'm sure he and Bev think you want a cut of their kids' inheritance. Everything revolves around money for them. But Ed having a secret child didn't surprise me at all. I'm just embarrassed about the way he's treated you. It's been shameful."

Yet another relative agreed with that assessment. "There is a right way and a wrong way to handle this and he's handling it poorly. Just think about all the sneaking around and secrecy that could have been avoided if he would have just been open about you from the beginning. It's so much easier to smile about something and be happy about it than to be angry and fight."

There was discussion about my girls and how badly they felt for them. "It's like they have been chucked out into the cold. There are people in this family who would love to have a grandchild and here's Edward tossing three of them away like they were garbage.

I didn't know someone could have too many grandkids but apparently they can."

Another relative quietly told me, "When I was told this news, I thought 'What if this kid is mine?'" He turned to me. "I want you to know that I was fully prepared to accept you into my family. I would have been happy to have been your father. I'm proud being your uncle."

When I smiled at him, the ends of my lips quivered. I cleared my throat. "Thank-you."

"I was watching you," he continued. "You walked up my driveway and you were laughing. All I could see was my brother. Then you sat down across from me and as we've been talking, I realized the reason why you're so easy to talk to is because I feel like I'm talking with Edward. You two are like two peas in a pod."

I chuckled. "Two peas, yes. In a pod, no."

I was surprised at how many of these new people were just as nervous about possible rejection as I was. "I've noticed from Facebook that you're a Democrat," a cousin told me. "I figure I should just tell you right now that I'm a Republican."

"Good for you," I said, smiling. "You know, I didn't search twenty-five years for you guys only to hope that you would be just like me. My family and I are interested in knowing who you are—no matter what."

After speaking to relative after relative, I discovered that most of them had the same experience with Edward where they used to be close to him, but things had changed. "He used to be my favorite." "We used to be very close." "We talked all the time, every week." "We had so much fun when we were younger." And then things took a turn ... "But not anymore." "I haven't spoken to him in two years." "I don't know what is going on with him now." "He just stopped caring."

The Schneyder Family had been fractured since their father died and no one that I spoke with escaped without battle scars. Their mother had Alzheimer's and although she didn't pass away until two years after their father, it was definitely in losing their dad when things shifted and the divide began.

I listened as my new relatives recounted memories. Each one told me about when their dad died and it was interesting to hear how they described their role during the passing of their father. It was also fascinating to see how they viewed the roles of their siblings, especially where Edward was involved. He was the executor of the will. He was under a lot of pressure from the voices of his dead parents to the stress of his arguing siblings. The aftermath of their father's death cracked that divide deeper. Then came caring for their mother until her death. After that, they all split.

"If my dad was alive, he would have loved you," one relative proclaimed. "If he were here, I guarantee you and Ed would have a relationship."

I nodded. I had wondered about that. If I had found Edward ten years before when my grandparents were still living, would things have turned out different? Would my grandparents have wanted to know me? Would they have accepted me? And if they had, would Edward eventually have come around?

I tried to not think those thoughts too much. They were maddening.

"How has it been meeting so many of us?" another relative asked.

"Exhausting," I replied.

It was. There were five of us and a gazillion of them. And because so many of my new aunts and uncles didn't speak to others, we often had to go up and meet with individuals separately. It was time-consuming and required commitment and work from us.

Every time we returned from meeting someone, it took days to decompress. Meeting a new family member was like finding another counterpart to my soul. I'd sit across from a new relative and I would see my crazy side in their crazy side. I would sense a similar thought pattern with another. I would notice I had the same hands as this uncle or the same eyes as that cousin. The Schneyder family was full of teachers and multi-generations of those who were masters of a craft, sharing their art in different media, from woodworkers to painters. We discovered cousins who taught foreign language—which was what Rosie studied. We learned of their love for music and that Edward played in the high school band—percussion, just like Catey. These people had my sense of humor. They were quick, rash, sarcastic, and sharp. I was surprised at how quickly I gravitated to them, how fast my comfort level was achieved as I entered homes and hearts. Sometimes it was as if I had always known them, as if something inside of me at a cellular level remembered who they were. And that they were my tribe

Finding the Schneyders had been both heartwarming and heartbreaking. The more I spent with my new found family, listening to their stories of what was and what would never be, I could see pain in each of their eyes. Each one of my new aunts and uncles were saddened by the way their family had turned out. They all claimed they wanted to pick up the phone and call their siblings and tell them that they loved them and that they were sorry for wrongs that were done way before I ever showed up in their world. But the more I got to know them, the more I understood that those were just words and that no one held any action behind them. There would be no calls placed and no amends made.

All of them - all ten of them - had given up on one or more of their own siblings. That was hard for me to witness. Each one was so full of love and acceptance for me and yet many of them refused to be in the same room with one another. Anger had eaten away at their foundation where they all proclaimed they were once a strong family. Now they were weak. From the view point of an intruder who was just meeting them, I felt kinship, love, and sadness for them.

Family Weekend at Rosie's school, the University of Northern Iowa, was held the first weekend of November. We enjoyed two days with the Schneyders watching a Panthers football game, eating Mexican food, and meeting more relatives. The Sunday after, we drove to a small town in Iowa and met my great-uncle Maurice. He was my biological grandfather Schneyder's youngest brother. Maurice had heard about us through his own family, who had learned about us secondhand.

The minute we pulled into the driveway, Maurice opened the screen door to the side of his house and waved us in. "Come!" he shouted. "Come in!"

We looked over at him and the girls, still in the van, started yelling, "Oh, my God! Look at him! That's Dad! That's Dad in forty years!"

I got out of the van and walked over. The resemblance was undeniable.

I stuck my hand out. Maurice slapped it away and brought me in for an embrace. He held me there for a few seconds, and when he broke away, he pointed to his nose and then mine. "Same," he smiled. His eyes traveled beyond me and he called out, "Come in! Girls! Come inside!"

We clamored into the house and met his wife, Lucy, who offered us something to drink. Maurice sat us down, while he stood in between all of us, telling stories about the Schneyder family. We followed him downstairs where he had stacks of photo albums ready to share. Maurice handed over newspaper clippings, articles, and family photographs. "Ask me anything," he challenged. He happily and easily answered our questions.

At one point, Maurice sat in his rocker, folded his hands over his stomach, and looked me dead in the eyes. "Michael, is your mother alive?"

The question took me by surprise. "Yes, she is," I replied.

He stopped rocking. "How is she doing with all of this?"

"She's ..." I hesitated, "getting there."

"That's good," he nodded. "This can't be easy for her."

"No, it's not."

Maurice turned to my girls. "How are all of you doing?"

The girls answered separately. "It's been tough." "I feel rejected." "It makes me sad sometimes."

Maurice stood and dragged a kitchen chair over to the girls. He sat in front of them. "You see, Edward is having a hard time, too," he said. "He's got a lot on his plate over at his house. Imagine you are his wife and you've been married for forty years and you suddenly find out about this joker," he thumbed over at me. "Everything you have ever known has suddenly been turned upside down. What you thought was true, isn't anymore. It's like someone came up behind Bev and hit her over the head with a frying pan. She's stunned. She's dazed. She's seeing stars." He nodded at the girls. "None of that is your fault and none of it is your dad's fault. But it's not Bev's fault, either. The thing is, though, everyone has to wait until the stars start to clear. Everyone has to wait on Bev."

It was in that moment that I realized that these simple questions Maurice was asking us—How is your mom doing? Is she alive? How are you feeling? Girls, how are you dealing? Edward never asked me any of those things. The entire time I talked with him, he never once asked about my mother. He never asked if she was even alive or how she was doing or what her life was like. He certainly didn't ask about my children. He barely asked about my well-being. All he cared about was who had I told, who did I think knew about me in Lawrence, who was I talking to in his family, and how Bev was losing her shit. *I'm the victim in this situation...*

Huh. There was a right way and a wrong way of doing all this.

And here was an eighty-five-year-old man doing it right.

I swallowed and asked Maurice the question I had been wanting to ask all of my new-found family members, "Should I keep trying?" I kept telling myself that even with everything I had done, all Edward and Bev needed was more time. I just needed to get a foot in the door to one of my half-brothers—if one of them met me, surely they would fall in love with me and my family and they would put in the good word for us.

Maurice put a gentle hand up, hushing my thoughts. "Just let it be."

* *
* *

We met up with Aunt Carolyn one weekend and she told us that after everyone had received the damage-control phone call from Edward they also received a phone call from Marty. While Edward's conversation had been calm, as he recalled his underwear story and encouraged his family not to talk to me, the call from Marty was frantic, outraged, and full of threats.

"Marty told me that you are a liar, that Amy is wicked, your mother was basically a . . . a whore, and that your girls shouldn't exist."

I glanced at Amy and the girls, who were listening in. Amy sighed and sarcastically said, "Wow. Well, it sounds like Marty is angry so I guess that means he still cares!"

Carolyn went on, "He told us that we were NOT to speak to you and that you were all a bunch of atheists!"

"No, we're not!" I countered back, angry that this was what was brought up. I didn't believe in God and, as I feared, this is what would be used against me and my family. It didn't matter if I was a successful person, a productive member of society, or a good dad. All that was lost because I didn't believe in a higher power. "Four out of five of us believe in God." It was all I had. Amy and the girls were believers and I knew Carolyn was very faith-filled.

Aunt Carolyn didn't seem bothered by the news at all. She was onto the next thing on Marty's list. "He told me I was to hang up the phone with him and call Ed and tell him everything you have ever told me."

I shrugged. "Edward can call me anytime. I will tell him everything I have told you guys. I haven't told you anything I wouldn't tell him." I paused. "Did he actually say whore?" I asked.

"Marty said that Ed told him that your mom had slept with all the guys in the house that night and that he was just the last one she got to. Of course, Ed also said there was never any penetration between the two of them, though."

I looked away. I had no words. My mind raced to old family photos of my mother when she was growing up. I could see her with her short black hair, chubby cheeks, standing next to my Aunt Susan. Her deep-set eyes held a sparkle, and her smile was tender. I tried imagining her as a teenager, entering and exiting room after room in a rented house with five men. I couldn't do it. I tried to imagine her drunk or stoned. My mom jumping from guy to guy, sober or intoxicated, just didn't seem to match who I knew her to be. At her core, she was a timid person. I would describe her as shy, not a risk-taker, and definitely a one-man-woman.

"Okay, so," Amy put her hands up, trying to understand, "what Marty is saying is Diane walked in the door that night—she may as well have shown up wearing her bra and underwear. She tramped in, strolled around the circle of guys and was like 'Hi, Boys! My name is Diane! I'm seventeen years old! A junior in high school! I'm five-foot-one-inch tall, one hundred ten pounds! I like tacos and dogs! My hymen is intact! And I'm HERE TO GET PREGNANT!'" Amy cracked up. It was a little hysterical. "Jesus Christ! He makes it sound like she asked for it."

I couldn't process. My emotions were coming in waves. It was like I was in a tunnel, falling through it, all these people, believing Edward's story, swirling around me, laughing, making fun that I was here. Blaming me, blaming my mom, blaming my wife, blaming my kids. And now this? What Edward was saying was I was conceived because my teenage mother sexually assaulted him, against his will, he didn't have sex with her, and yet she became pregnant miraculously.

I was the chosen one. An atheist born from Immaculate Conception. What bullshit.

I closed my eyes and I could hear Edward's voice when I was on the phone with him, telling him the little I had about my mother—*"she dropped out of high school, couldn't go to college, had a pretty tough time of it, had to work two and three jobs . . ."* And his response, *"I didn't need to know all of that."*

The room got quiet. I was feeling suffocated by it. Carolyn spoke up, her voice both soft and sharp to my ears, "Ed and Marty both said the same thing about you, though."

I scrubbed a hand down my face. "What's that?"

"They said you might be Ed's son but you would never be a Schneyder."

I nodded. In Edward's mind, I would never be pure enough to be a genuine Schneyder. I was always my mother's. Not his. Not then and not now.

I could forgive *then* Edward. I didn't know if I could forgive *now* Edward.

FORTY-TWO

Ghost·ing

\ gōstiNG \ noun

    1. The appearance of a ghost or secondary image on
       a television or other display screen.

    2. The practice of ending a personal relationship
       with someone by suddenly and without explanation
       withdrawing from all communication.

Definitely #2, but I wondered if it was actually considered ghosting if there had never been an established relationship in the first place. Either way, Edward and my half-brothers had decided the best way to deal with me was to act as if I did not exist.

It was hard to accept that.

In September 2018, while we were in peak reunion with the Schneyders, the hearing for Brett Kavanaugh to become a Supreme Court Justice began. Dr. Christine Blasey Ford had accused the nominee of sexual misconduct while they were in high school together. It had been more than thirty years ago. It was a fascinating trial for me to follow because whether I meant to or not, my mind wandered from their story to my mother and Edward. The legal team grilling Dr. Ford about what she remembered and over and over again, asking her if she was one hundred percent certain it was Brett Kavanaugh who had groped her. She was sure. She seemed sure. She seemed pretty damn credible.

Then Kavanaugh's turn. He brought in a calendar from high school that he had used as a journal with scribbles of football practices and hanging out with friends. His calendar was full of spy names and code words. Throughout the trial, he denied the allegations and in the end, Dr. Ford came up with no proof of her sexual assault and, of course, now Brett is known as Justice Kavanaugh.

From the beginning of the trial, it was going to end this way. Dr. Ford never had a chance because, as my youngest daughter, Jillian, pointed out, Ford didn't have any "receipts." Ah, receipts—proof of purchase or proof that someone is lying. Dr. Ford didn't have any receipts to prove her case.

My mother, on the other hand, had a huge receipt: Me.

Half of America believing Kavanaugh's story was something that I understood. How anyone in the Schneyder family could believe Edward's story was beyond me.

Ironically, through my research and after talking to other adoptees, I found that there are many of us conceived this way. Men claimed this defense over and over. "I was near the goal but it never went in!" "I had my jeans on!" "We only danced one song!" "I never even met your mother."

There are thousands of us.

There comes a point in the discovery process where you have to find peace and that begins with choosing the story that you decide is close enough to the truth. No one is ever going to know their exact origin story, we all have to accept and embrace our own uncertainty, but eventually, especially for those of us who were born with a question mark, we have to come to our own conclusion.

I held on to facts.

My mom was seventeen. She was a junior in high school. She lived at home with my grandparents. I believed she had sex with

Edward twice—my medical records mentioned my birth was difficult because of her inexperience. She dropped out of high school. She worked two jobs to support me. She was the one who stuck with me.

I also believed my grandparents. They had no reason to lie to me and everything that they told me paralleled what my mother claimed. I believed they met Edward in 1971 when he arrived to pick up my mom, and I believe that five years later, he drove up their driveway, and asked if my mom ever had the baby. That was the story I deemed as true.

However, in Edward's defense, I think he got scared. I believe my mother told him she was pregnant and shortly after that, he packed his stuff up and moved his ass back to Lawrence. I am sure that in his nineteen-year-old brain, he told himself that she surely slept around, there was no way that I could be his. And then as the years went by, I didn't show up, nobody knocked on his door and I think he thought he was in the clear. Obviously, somebody else was the kid's father.

Either that or he truly forgot about the interactions with my mother. He wholeheartedly has no memory of her. Or of me. Somehow, life, time, age, alcohol, whatever . . . was either erased or suppressed.

So, I do believe that he was genuinely surprised when I popped up on Ancestry. I am certain I was everything he feared I would be—successful, happy, and, his. He had no reason to not want to know me but every reason to push me away. I believe he had no other choice because if Bev and his sons knew my mother's story, they would for sure realize that his version of events was a sham.

AncestryDNA, 23 and Me, and My Heritage, along with other DNA test sites, are literally turning people's worlds upside down. For those searching, these tests are answering years-long mysteries for people who have spent their entire life searching for their birth families. They are a blessing, a last resort, a miracle.

For those who are being found, however, the result can be the exact opposite. They are living a carefree life, thinking they know exactly who they are and everything about their family until a little pink or blue icon pops up on their matches screen.

With such new technology disrupting lives left and right, I have come to understand that the problem seems to be that these people who are being found simply don't know what to do. They don't know how to react. It scares the shit out of them. Mostly these "surprise people" are biological fathers and biological half-siblings. When they are contacted by a new, close family member, they have no idea how to start communicating in a way that can help everyone effectively move forward.

For me, my choice to tell my half-brothers was easy. My choice to send the announcement to my extended family was deliberate. The reason why I did these things was because I was tired of being a secret. There was no way I was going to carry the burden of Edward's embarrassment of me. I also understood that if I chose to walk away, that would have left Louisa, Carolyn, and his other siblings who knew about me, to carry the secret. Edward was willing to gamble on his remaining siblings, nephews/nieces, and his own sons finding out secondhand, instead of him revealing the truth to them.

Even in the wake of my disappointment, knowing that my half-brothers have never wanted to meet me, I have nothing but a clear conscience, knowing that they were worth the truth. Even if the truth had to come from me.

*
* *

Amy and I drove into Lawrence on a Friday afternoon. We wandered around the town square and stopped into a restaurant for a late lunch. The people around us appeared to be locals, sitting with their families, talking easily to the waitress, and side-eyeing us every so often. They knew strangers when they saw them.

We plugged in the location to the cemetery where my grandparents were buried and we grabbed the bouquet of flowers I had bought the day before. Their graves were easy to find as they faced the small circle road we had driven down. I walked over and gazed at them. Time doesn't wait for the living. It wasn't the way I imagined meeting either one of them but, as I looked around, they seemed to have a great view. I closed my eyes and tried to feel something there, some kind of presence, a connection, anything.

The wind kicked up and whipped around my body, my jeans fluttered and my shirt ruffled away from my sides. I opened my eyes and saw a streak of sunlight highlighting the name Schneyder on top of the stone. I felt my eyes prick for a second and I shrugged my shoulders. It was as close to a "Hello" as I needed.

"How far away is Edward's house?" I asked Amy as we got back in the car. I chose to take the passenger seat and let her drive.

Amy checked the address. "One mile."

"Let's drive by it." I pointed to the right and Amy turned the wheel.

Edward's neighborhood was very nice and filled of mostly new homes. I knew that several of the houses in his area had been damaged by the flood and where he lived were newer construction homes, including his.

Amy came down a slight hill, heading to a four-way crossing. "This is it up here on the right," she said as she slowed down. The house sat up high. It was exactly what I expected him to live in—it was classy and timeless. There was a large lawn surrounding the house and a shed out back. The attached garage looked like it would be the perfect mancave.

As Amy crept by the side of the house, the front yard started to come into our view. There, on a riding lawn mower was Edward, driving down the hill of his front yard, heading right for the four-way stop, right where we were going to meet up with him in five short seconds.

"Oh, my God!" Amy panicked. "What do I do? What do I do?"

I shook my head. "There's nothing you can do. Just keep on going."

We moved forward and as we approached the four corners, Edward arrived on his mower. My window was down and as he looked up, we met once again. He was wearing a ball cap, sunglasses, a t-shirt and shorts. I was wearing the exact same thing.

I gave him a half nod and smiled.

Amy stopped and slowly started to turn to the left. Edward stared hard at me. If I had put my hand out, we could have high-fived. The look on his face was somewhere between pissed and murder. Amy made the left and we drove on. I looked in the rearview mirror and saw Edward, still sitting in the same position, not moving at all. As our van sped up, I could feel his anger chasing after me.

I didn't blame him. This time I deserved for him to be mad at me. I had purposefully driven to his turf. I could only imagine the fearful thoughts racing through his mind—What was I going to do? Would I park? Get out of the car? Knock on their door? Teepee his house?

The possibilities were endless.

I watched him sitting there, motionless, until he disappeared from my sight.

FORTY-THREE

I made five trips to the Polk County Clerk of Court in 2019.

Amy and I were going on our first vacation since having children, twenty-one years prior. It was in celebration of our twenty-fifth wedding anniversary, so we thought we would treat ourselves and booked a cruise to Alaska, with a stop in Victoria, British Columbia. Neither of us had ever been on a cruise or out of the country, so one of our first priorities was to fill out the proper paperwork for our passports. Amy received hers two weeks after we mailed them. Mine was delayed because of my birth certificate. I went to the post office and the clerk told me she had never seen a birth certificate like mine. In return, I was given a list of things I could present to prove my identity. On the list:

1. Provide a family bible with the entry of your name and birth.
2. A circumcision certificate.
3. A notarized statement from an older, blood relative who is able to verify your birth.

I stared at these requests. What if I were a female, atheist, who was adopted and didn't know any older, blood relatives? These requests were ridiculous.

However, I remembered the medical records from my birth contained a certificate of circumcision. Twenty years before, I had giggled at the document and now I was placing it gingerly into a folder and walking into the Polk County Clerk of Court, hoping it would be an acceptable document in obtaining my passport so I could spend a day in Canada.

Six weeks later, my passport arrived in the mail. I dangled it in front of Amy. "I can't believe I had to show proof of my circumcision just so I could go on vacation!"

JULY 2019

The vacation itself was amazing. We spent one week on the cruise and another four days in Seattle. My Aunt Louisa and Uncle Henry lived in the area, as did their son Geo and his family.

Every one of those four days we were with my new family. Aunt Louisa and Uncle Henry chauffeured us around the city, showing us the sites. We ventured to Roslyn, Washington, which is ironically the namesake of our daughter Rosie. We walked up to Snoqualmie Falls and we drove down to Tacoma.

I spent time with my cousin Geo, who, like me, was a professor at a local university. I had read the tributes of those who claimed getting to know their bio-family was easy because "we just clicked." That was how I felt with Geo. I had never met him before this day and within two hours, it was like I had known him my whole life. Geo had an ease about him and when I looked at him, I saw bits and pieces of myself staring back. He took me and Amy out for breakfast one morning, touring us around one of his favorite spots. We walked along the side streets where people would stop. "Geo! How are you!?"

Geo would swagger their way. "Hey, Bob. I'm good. Let me introduce you to my cousin Michael."

Just like that. So easy for him. Not a hesitation or a stutter. "My cousin" with a smile on his face and a twinkle in his eyes. Bob put his hand out to me, "Nice to meet you."

I nodded and shook his hand, "You, too." Out of the corner of my eye, I saw Geo standing near me, smiling. He waved at another friend and then pointed at me. "Hey, Joe! How's it going? Come over here, I want you to meet my cousin Michael!"

I swallowed hard and blinked the water out of my eyes. Cousin Geo . . . he made my fucking day.

Many of our trips with Louisa and Henry included seeing exhibits of glass, such as our trip to the Chihuly Museum of Glass where Amy and I walked through the building in awe of the beauty surrounding us. We also ventured down to Tacoma for a viewing of a glass exhibit at the Museum of Glass. It was there that we had the opportunity to watch glass blowers in action in a hot shop.

The Glass Museum in Tacoma was featuring the story *Raven Steals the Sun* in which a Raven, who existed from the beginning of time, was tired of living his life in the dark. He finds an old man, living with his daughter, and discovers that the old man is hiding a great treasure. It was all the light in the universe. The Raven, wanting to steal the treasure, came up with a plan where he transformed himself into a needle and dropped into a river where the old man's daughter was drinking. The girl drinks the Raven, who slithers into her belly and transforms into a tiny human, which the girl gives birth to. The old man loves his grandson but warns him to stay away from his treasure. He shields him from the contents until one day, after much begging, the old man opens the lid of the box. He grabs the light of the universe and tosses it to his grandson, like it was a game of catch, expecting the child to throw it back. Instead, his grandson suddenly transforms into a gigantic, black raven, wings spread, ready for the light, his beak opens—and he captures the beautiful ball! Then he beats his powerful wings and escapes from his grandfather's home into the darkness of the world, where he soared high up to the sky. And that is how light came into the universe.

I walked alongside Amy, Aunt Louisa, and Uncle Henry and read the story. I took pictures, I absorbed the quiet and I let the warmth wash over me. I held on to the fragile balance that as I was here in this moment, with these three purposely placed people, one who had gone on the ups and downs of a twenty-five year journey with me to discover the other two. It was in that moment that I realized I was the Raven. No longer in the dark, having stolen the treasure that had been hidden from me for so long, and now my universe was finally engulfed in light.

FORTY-FOUR

The lightning bugs surrounding my Aunt Carolyn's house were plentiful, the trees north of her property lit up in waves of orange and gold, like the bugs were performing a private light show just for us. Uncle Randy walked way into the woods and let off a cherry bomb, without warning, causing us all to jump out of our chairs and run to the end of their wrap-around porch. He came out of the brush, a ball of smoke trailing behind him, grinning like a bandit.

We all broke into laughter.

As the night wound down, we gathered at Carolyn and Randy's dining table. Our girls asked their new great-aunt and uncle if either of them had any funny stories about Edward. Our girls hung onto every word when we talked and they loved to hear fun stories of the grandfather they didn't know.

Carolyn and Randy thought about it for a moment and then Randy said, "Oh, I got one, I got one." He laughed. "Ed would probably kill me if he knew I told you this but it's funny." He laughed, just thinking about it and we all leaned in. "One time when we were down in Florida—Ed and Bev were staying in the same condo complex as we were—and they had drove down in their car. Well, Ed's car had a problem with the transmission, and he had to take it in to have it looked at. Ed dropped it off at a dealership and days went by but he never heard anything so he called them up and asked about his car. The guy told him his car was finished and gave him a ridiculous amount of money due—three thousand dollars or something to pick it up. Well, Ed thought that was way too much and he wasn't going to pay for it. So the next morning, I wake up at six a.m. to a knock on my door. I open it and there's Ed. He tells me to get dressed, that he needs a ride. So, I get dressed and we get in my car and Ed tells me to take him to the dealership. As I'm driving, he says that the place never called him because they didn't have his correct phone number written down and they didn't even have his name right. Ed says they didn't have enough info on him to pin him down or anything and Ed still had his key fob on him because he had left his key with the mechanic—who needs a key these days, right? So, Ed had me drive up to the dealership and he hopped out of my car and ran around back. About three minutes later here he comes, driving his car off the lot. Son of a bitch—stole his own car! And they never found him. He totally got away with it!" Randy laughed. "I mean it's not funny, but it's funny."

"Yeah," we agreed. "That was quite a story."

We continued on with dinner, talking about other people and other things but later, as we drove home that night, I was having a difficult time relaxing. Amy offered to drive so I could try to catch a little sleep but my thoughts were, once again, screaming in my brain. I turned to her. "That was some story Randy told us."

"Yeah," she agreed.

"I don't know why but I can't shake it from my mind."

Amy nodded. "That's because it's your story."

I frowned.

"Your mom was the dealership and you were the bill that Edward skipped out on. He knew the dealership didn't have enough info about him to nail him and so he snuck in the back, took what he wanted, and ran away. Like he was never there. The dealership did all the work and Edward stuck them with the bill."

My mind was blown. "That asshole has been doing this shit his whole life!"

Amy nodded. "Yeah. Probably."

We drove on. The girls had passed out, Bob Seger was singing *Night Moves* on the radio, but my mind was racing as the words my new relatives had used to describe Edward were skipping along like a broken record.

Crook. Cheap. He probably thinks you want his money.

"There's good in him," Amy said, like she could read my mind.

"You think?"

Amy looked in the rearview mirror at our girls, all sprawled out across the seats of the van. "Without you, there would be none of them and without Edward there would be no you. So, yeah," she smiled. "I'm sure."

OCTOBER 2019

On one of my many trips to the Clerk of Court, somewhere after acquiring my passport, but during the time I was working with the Iowa Adoptees Coalition, I started to question the clerks about my adoption. My questions were casual, I made it clear that I wasn't trying to obtain my sealed, original birth certificate but, rather, to find out if I was in fact adopted. My parents thought I was, but no one could locate any paperwork. It was on one of those visits where the woman helping me said, "You know, all of your requests have been through vital records. I don't think you want us. You need to go upstairs to juvenile records." She gave me a name of a person to talk to, so I sprinted up the stairs and talked to the clerk there.

"Fill this out." The lady handed me a simple three question paper:

Name: Michael Blair, Date of Birth: February 18, 1972

Reason for Request ... I hesitated and then quickly wrote: "Everyone deserves the right to know where they come from."

I handed it back to her.

"I know that you guys probably can't release my records—"

"That's up to a judge to decide."

"Yeah," I said. "I know. What I'm really wanting to know if someone can look in the computer and just tell me *if* I'm adopted. I'm not requesting paperwork right now or anything, I just want to know is there an actual adoption tied to my name."

The lady glanced up at me. She looked tired. "You'll hear back from someone next week."

I shrugged. "Okay." She clearly was not able to help me and I had no idea why I was even there. What a waste of time.

Next week came. Nothing.

The Friday after, Amy texted me and suggested I call their offices. I looked at the time—it was 3:30pm, there was no way anyone was going to be there, but I called anyway. The lady who had helped me the previous Friday answered right away.

"Hi," I said, caught a little off guard. "I was checking the status of my adoption records request?"

"Name?"

"Michael Blair."

There was some typing and then, very calmly she said, "Your request is with the judge. You will hear from him in two to four weeks."

"Oh. Okay."

She hung up. I stared out into space for a few minutes. I never thought that the paper I had filled out was an official request for anything. This isn't going to go well, I thought. I had completed the form in such a rush, there was no way a judge was going to take me seriously. I was never going to be granted anything.

Two weeks later, I received a phone call at work from the clerk of court telling me my file was ready to be picked up. I looked across the room at my co-worker, Melissa, and I said, "I have to go. The judge granted my request."

Melissa knew exactly what I was talking about. She smiled and shooed me away. "Go! Go!"

I drove straight down to the Polk County Records Building and walked in with a confidence I had never had before. I felt like I owned the place. I walked up to the distribution window and the clerk typed my name in. "You need to go up to payments and pay first," she told me. "I need a receipt before I can give it to you."

"How much is it?"

She scrolled. "Six dollars."

This time I ran up the stairs, taking two at a time. I paid the bill, receipt in hand, and went back down to the window. I handed the clerk my proof of purchase and in return, she handed me a Manila envelope.

"Have a nice day," she offered with a lackluster smile.

"I will!" I grinned. I pointed my finger at her. "I hope you do, too!"

She chuckled, shook her head, and returned to her typing.

I walked to my car, buckled up the envelope in the passenger seat, and drove home. I sat down with Amy and we opened it up. There were a dozen pages to my adoption file—my adoption! I was legally adopted! I let out a relieved breath. Even if I hadn't been legally adopted, it wouldn't have changed anything, but I really was adopted. My dad wanted me to be his. As a young man, he went through hoops and bounds to be sure that I was legally his son. I rubbed my heart.

A lot of the papers were boring legal jargon about who I was and who had custody of me. The adoption was initiated in 1976 but wasn't finalized until 1979. During that time, my mother had three different addresses listed, the first where she was living with my grandparents, the second after she moved into the apartment with my dad, and the third, after they bought their house. No wonder they didn't have any paperwork on my adoption. Who knows what address it was sent to?

The first thing we noticed was there was no original birth certificate in the file. However, there was an interim birth certificate, which contained more information than my delayed copy. I could tell from the interim one that my mother had not named anyone as my father. I wasn't surprised. It stated my original birth certificate was requested to be sealed and had been granted by the Honorable Judge Glenn Blaschke. Another weird name. It also happened to be the maiden name of my Great-Grandmother Schneyder. Upon research, I found that Judge Blaschke was from the same county where Edward resided.

Had Edward known about me, after all? Had he shown up when I was five and been so scared from my grandfather that he called in a favor from a distant relative? Did he fear that my mom had named him on my birth certificate? Or was it all just a weird coincidence? I went with the latter and moved on. One thing I had learned throughout this journey was asking yourself too many questions will make you the Mayor of Crazy Town. It didn't matter one way or the other, so I let it go.

As we flipped through pages, we came to a section from 1977 where my mom provided her deposition to the court, regarding my biological father and answered questions that were asked by the clerk.

Last name of child's father?

"I do not know the last name of the father."

"Do you know the first name?"

"I know that I knew it back then but I can't remember it now. It was an easy name. It may have been John."

"Can you detail how you met Michael's father?"

And then my mother began the same story she had told me my entire life: *"I was walking by myself on Grand Avenue in the Spring of 1971. It was late in the afternoon when I met him. He was riding a motorcycle and was by himself also. I do not know any of his friends or relatives nor do any of my friends or relatives know him or his friends or relatives."*

I swallowed. It was the same. Her story that she told me in 1992 and again in 2017 was the same as the one she recounted in 1978. She didn't waiver. It was all the same. She just couldn't remember his name.

"I think his last name begins with an S." There it was, the exact way she recalled it to me.

The court ordered my mother to take an advertisement out in the newspapers. She complied and showed proof that she had done that, just like she told me she had. It was confirmed that no one came forward and answered the ad. The next page was dated September 20, 1977. It was a declaration that *I, Michael Lang, was deemed abandoned by his biological father, John Doe.* The court found that he had *substantially, continually, and repeatedly refused or neglected to comply with the duties imposed on him by the parent/child relationship.* It was then ordered that *the parental rights between John Doe and his minor child, Michael Lee Lang, be hereby terminated.*

Of course I knew all of this already, but to see it in black-and-white hit me like a punch in the gut.

I read "John Doe" but my heart knew the truth. Edward Schneyder. Even if I were to believe his story that he never knew I existed, from what I knew of him today, I don't believe his nineteen-year-old-self would have ever claimed me anyway. I was too inconvenient. I never had a place in his family, not then and not now.

The following page was my dad adopting me.

"On this day of January 30th, 1978, this matter comes up for hearing upon the verified Petition of the Petitioner, Craig Paul Blair. The Petitioner is the step-parent of the minor child herein sought for adoption and is qualified to adopt said child. Petitioner is desirous and able to adequately provide for, rear, and educate said minor child. He has prayed for the adoption and so it should be granted. From this day forward, the minor child, Michael Lee Lang, will have the surname of his natural mother and adoptive father and be henceforth known as Michael Lee Blair."

I swallowed again. It's a complicated feeling, this weird adoption thing. There is so much joy in it and such sorrow at the same time. Who would I have been if my biological father would have stuck? How would Michael Schneyder be different from Michael Blair? Or Michael Lang? How much does a person change based on the presence or the omittance of one person in their life? Would I even want to know the other person I could have been? Because, you know what? Diane and Craig Blair did a pretty fucking good job. My chest swelled. Twelve pages of a history of two people who loved me so much that as kids, they chose to do right by me. They may have had rough patches and regrets, but who doesn't? Life wasn't supposed to be perfect, it was often unsatisfactory and messy. These were my parents, one biologically and one by choice.

I am Michael Blair. For the first time in forty-seven years, I was letting go of the burden I associated with my name and instead of wondering who else I was, I was becoming content with who I had always been my entire life.

FORTY-FIVE

On a beautiful late summer evening, I sat on the patio with my best friend, Shawne. Our chairs were faced toward the vast woods in the back of his property, a fire pit off to our side, and a bottle of wine sitting between us.

The sun began to set. "So," Shawne probed. He tipped his head in a questioning manner. "Are you glad you did the DNA test? Or do you wish you had never done it?"

If someone asked me, "What is the number-one question you get asked about your journey?" It is this one—*Are you happy you did it or do you regret it?* Without any doubt, I am happy I did it. Living with the question mark was worse than living with the truth. I have answers. I know the name of my biological father. I was fortunate enough to talk to him, to meet him, to shake his hand. Edward gave more than a lot of discovered bio-fathers do—he took a DNA test with me. He gave me the gift of knowing.

I think the question people should ask is, "If you had to do it all again, would you do anything different?"

Yes.

In the beginning, I would have been quiet. With that, I mean my family and I would not have told our friends and family as soon as we did. I would have waited to talk to Edward's siblings until after

Edward had made his final decision in telling me to get lost. While I viewed moving forward with his siblings as my right, Edward saw it as a betrayal.

Finding the answer to a question that had followed me for forty-five years, though, just overcame me. Amy and I were giddy with excitement and overzealous with the news. In hindsight, that wasn't what Edward wanted or needed. I doubt that keeping quiet and waiting him out would have resulted in any other outcome—Edward was never going to move forward with a friendship with me—but maybe he would have felt he had more control of his own hand. No one puts their heart into something when they feel they are being forced into it.

I looked at Shawne. "One hundred percent, I would do it again. Searching for him was one of the best decisions I ever made, even during the worst of it."

"How do you feel about them now?" Shawne didn't define "them" but I knew he meant Edward, Bev, and my brothers. "Are you angry or do you hate them? Or do you just not care anymore?"

"None of the above," I replied. Strangely, my heart had not been jaded. How could it be? My family had grown and the love that came along with it had expanded how I viewed my past, present, and future. On the first day of my journey, looking over Amy's shoulder as she typed in the Schneyder name, I told her anyone who wanted to know me would be a bonus.

I found my bonus. And multiplied that by about thirty.

"I have nothing but love for them."

Shawne smirked. He seemed skeptical. "But, I mean, Bev is the villain of the story, right? If she wasn't around, you would probably have a relationship with Edward. Don't you think?"

I smiled. Funny thing about a journey is your point of view seems to mature as time goes on. In the beginning, Edward had told me that he thought he was the victim in this story. I didn't see it that way. In 1971, my mother was the victim and in 2017, the victim of this story was Bev. She was the one who had been blindsided.

Trauma comes in many forms. I had been through some pretty deep shit over the past twenty-eight years of my journey and since spitting in that tube, Bev had dealt with her own trauma. She and I were both casualties of the actions of my mother and her husband. When I received my AncestryDNA results, it wasn't just my life that changed, many lives were changed. Not all for the better.

From the moment I showed up, Bev was building her walls and loading her guns. She was tough as nails and made every move Edward attempted in getting to know me extremely difficult. I like difficult women. And Bev was no different. From everything that I had been told, she had the men in her life by their balls and commanded their loyalty to her. How could I not respect that?

But I wasn't her son and she didn't have me under her thumb, like she had the rest of them. I didn't have to play by her rules. I would not bend to Edward or Bev's wishes. I refused to be a secret when all Bev wanted was for me to go away. I wasn't going to be hidden any longer.

I looked at Shawne and replied, "No, Bev is not the villain. The villain of my story is the secret."

And because I am the secret, in a roundabout way, I am also the villain. At least in Edward and Bev's version of the story. But this isn't Edward's story anymore. It's not Bev's story. It isn't my mother's. Now, I am the owner of the story. Really, it has always been mine.

"It sounds like you are doing a lot better," Shawne said. "I guess that means you have achieved peace and closure."

"Peace, yes." I nodded. "Closure, no."

While seeking closure, I had come to the conclusion that there would never be any. Closure doesn't exist for many of us because this is a fluid situation. It's in constant motion. There is no bottom to be reached. Whether Edward wants to join or not, I still have an ongoing relationship with the Schneyders and with that brings a road in front of me that is both smooth and bumpy. I have made a conscious decision to stay the course with these people. With that I have accepted that I will never have closure.

And, surprisingly, I'm okay with that decision. Closure is intended to end something, to shut down a chapter. Personally, I don't feel closed at all. I feel wide open.

"Where do you go from here?" Shawne poured another glass of wine and sat back.

"Forward. I'm going to stick with those who want to know me," I told him. "And my door will remain open for those who haven't walked through it yet."

Shawne laughed. "How much do you think it would take for Edward and your brothers to get a foot in that door?"

I stared at him hard and answered honestly, "It wouldn't take much."

*
* *

My dad handed me his phone. "I can't get it to work."

Of all the times my parents called me, half of the phone calls were because they couldn't get something to work in their house.

I turned it on and scrolled to settings and within three minutes I handed it back to him.

"Well, all be damned." My dad stared at his working phone as if I had given him a brick of gold. "Thank you, Mike."

"No problem."

My dad raised his eyes and met mine. As he aged, his eyes had become soft, along with the rest of him. "You know, I want to tell you that I have regret for not telling you sooner that I adopted you. Your mother and I should have been open about it and told you from the beginning."

I didn't know what to say. I could immediately see that he meant every word. "It was a long time ago," I said. It was, that was true. And it wasn't.

"Well, I wanted to say that I'm sorry about how we handled it."

"You guys were young." I was taken off-guard at the apology. "You did the best you could."

My dad agreed with that. "He have hair?" He asked bashfully. "Your biological father? Does he have hair?"

I smiled. "Yeah, Dad. He does."

"Huh. I thought he would be bald, like you."

"Nope. He can definitely get a brush through his hair."

My dad chuckled. "He have your skinny legs?"

I looked down. All my life people had remarked about how thin my ankles were and that I had inherited Tina Turner's legs. "Yeah, he has skinny legs. Most of my aunts and uncles do, too."

"We used to say that Michael looked like a marshmallow stuck on top of two toothpicks."

I laughed. "Yes, I remember that—thanks for reminding me."

My dad quieted. "He, uh, never wanted to get to know you?"

I shook my head. "No, he didn't."

My dad frowned. "I don't get it. You're not a simpleton. You can hold a great conversation and you have interesting thoughts and ideas. You have a lot to contribute." He listed off my good qualities like he was taking out an ad in the singles column of a newspaper. "How could that man not want to know my boy?" He slowly turned away, his back facing me. He looked small and his shoulders seemed heavy, like they were carrying years of guilt.

I remembered all the times as a kid when I did anything I could to be sure that I was the opposite of my dad. Now, I stood about a foot taller, fifty pounds heavier, and knew definitively that nothing in our genetic makeup said that we were related.

But in that moment, I felt closer to him than ever before. He needed someone to let him off the hook for the past. And I was just the person he needed.

I placed my hand quietly on his back and gave him a strong pat. "It's okay, Dad. I'm not mad anymore. I'm okay. You and I—we're okay. I'm proud to be your son."

FEBRUARY 2020

A rare afternoon—I was home alone. Amy and the girls were out running errands so I took advantage of a couple of hours to enjoy the quiet. I glanced at the date on my iPhone—the 8th of February. It had been just over three years since I received my AncestryDNA results.

I shook my head. Time flies when you're having fun.

I wandered into our living room and walked over to our mantel. Nestled among the many photos was a picture of my Grandma and Grandpa Lang. I picked it up and moved it to a side table. I chose a picture of my Grandma Peterson and moved her to the piano. Then I picked up a newly framed photo of my Grandma and Grandpa Schneyder and placed them high on the mantel. They held no more importance than my other grandparents but as I backed away, I thought it was time that they had the chance to sit atop the mantel and enjoy the view. It was their turn to watch over my family from the best view in the house.

I took a seat in my recliner and turned on the TV. A rerun of *30 Rock* was on. It was the episode where Jack Donaghy, played by Alec Baldwin, decides to search for his biological father. I shook my head. "Every damn show." Then I stayed still and watched it . . . and laughed. There was beauty in the struggle and there was humor in it, too. You just had to learn to put the anger and sadness aside to appreciate the good.

I repositioned myself in my chair and glanced around the room. The faces of my grandparents all looked out at me. I felt their connection, their pull. This journey had taught me that knowing who I was, where I came from, had provided me great empathy to those who came before. I felt rooted to all of them—both my birth family and my adopted one. None of them felt like strangers to me. They were all, simply, family.

The stories my mother and Edward told me about my conception no longer mattered to me. I believed what I chose and the rest didn't matter. I was here, wasn't I? Without the recklessness of two teenagers, I wouldn't have my wonderful life, my amazing daughters, and the chance to continue my own biological journey toward grandparenthood and beyond. I was thankful to Edward for his part but it was my dad who did what Edward could not do. He stepped up to the plate and adopted another man's child as his own. In my dad's eyes, I wasn't a burden, I was his bonus. And as for my mother, I would be indebted to her forever. She was the one who sacrificed. She was the one to whom I owed everything.

I worried about the future—about upcoming events and celebrations, which would include my mom, dad, and sisters in the same room as my newfound family members. I imagined them meeting, shaking hands or elbow bumps, talking in pleasant voices and wishing each other warm thoughts. I hoped they would mean it. I wanted them to get along.

My eyes fell on my Grandma and Grandpa Lang, my sight traveling over to my Grandma Peterson, and lastly to my Grandma and Grandpa Schneyder. None of them seemed to have a problem being in the same room together. They all looked content and happy, linked to each another by a common denominator: Me.

I eased back in the chair and smiled. I was one lucky bastard.

CPSIA information can be obtained
at www.ICGtesting.com
Printed in the USA
FSHW010737141020
74735FS